MW00626687

FINDING THE FOUNTAIN

FINDING THE FOUNTAIN

WHY GOVERNMENT MUST UNLOCK BIOTECH'S POTENTIAL TO MAXIMIZE LONGEVITY

BREANNA A. DEUTSCH

NEW DEGREE PRESS

COPYRIGHT © 2020 BREANNA A. DEUTSCH

All rights reserved.

FINDING THE FOUNTAIN
*Why Government Must Unlock Biotech's
Potential to Maximize Longevity*

ISBN   978-1-64137-916-8   *Paperback*

         978-1-64137-675-4   *Kindle Ebook*

         978-1-64137-677-8   *Ebook*

CONTENTS

_____

ACKNOWLEDGMENTS

This book was only made possible by the scientists, entrepreneurs, philanthropists, and activists who offered me their time and knowledge. I thank them for allowing me to include their stories and discoveries in this book, but most of all, I am grateful for the decades of research and immense energy and resources they have committed to finding treatments that will one day help alleviate human suffering.

INTRODUCTION

———

Health care is consistently a top voter priority. That is a non-controversial statement.

What should that health care look like? Well, that is one of the most contentious topics in Washington.

This book does not intend to comment on the ideal insurance model, nor does it offer a health care policy proposal that will finally please all sides of the aisle and swiftly move through the United States Congress and onto the president's desk. Instead, this book aims to find common ground among all Americans by outlining aspirational, long-term health care outcomes we can all agree on. Let's begin by imagining two potential scenarios:

A seventy-five-year-old man lays on a stiff mattress on a twin-sized hospital bed. He could do without the surrounding musty smell he hoped to escape when his dementia forced him out of the nursing home, but, nonetheless, he is grateful the nurses gave him a fresh blue gown after his "accident." With a new catheter in place and an IV dripping fluids into his bloodstream, he turns his attention back to the main activity of the day—staring at moving images on the screen. This is how he will spend the final days of his life. Frail, diseased, eating microwavable hospital meals from the confinement of his 38 x 75-inch bed.

Across the street from the hospital sits a popular community tennis court. All are welcome, but it is the main battleground for local amateur, elite players. On one side of the net is a forty-year-old man who played college tennis and has continued the sport recreationally throughout adulthood. On the other side of the court is a spry seventy-year-old woman known for her ruthless backhand serve. She did not pick up a racket until her early sixties, but quickly moved her name up the community scoreboard.

I will go ahead and assume that most Americans would choose to spend their final days living vigorously rather than staying alive only by the power of machines. Unfortunately, we cannot yet fully choose our final chapter, and for the majority of us, it reads like the first scenario, not the latter.

Most Americans accept that getting older—and eventually getting old—is part of the natural human cycle of life. Our bodies peak shortly before the age of thirty, and then a steady decline sets in until our mid-fifties, when our body's repair mechanisms begin to break down at an accelerated rate. With each passing year, we find deeper creases across our forehead, new pains in the curves of our back, we find ourselves scheduling more doctor visits, and watch as our medicine cabinets fill with enough prescription drugs to run our own apothecary. With US life expectancy now teetering close to eighty years, our time on Earth is growing longer, but it is handicapped by our decrepit state and soaring medical bills.

While we strive to have a long life, we all know that the gap of time between our birth and date of death engraved on our tombstone is not alone a measurement for a good life. Instead, what truly matters is a *healthy* life expectancy. This means how long we can enjoy a healthy, disability and disease-free existence.

The average American can expect to live just 67.7 *healthy* years.[1] In the decades we imagined filled with travel, previously side-lined hobbies, and newfound time, Americans instead find themselves spending their golden days and saved resources playing whack-a-mole with the various diseases of old age, popping prescriptions for their growing number of ailments, and relying heavily on family members to tend to their daily needs. This is not how we want to live, nor how we want to die.

While this is the current situation, it does not have to be the case. A pivotal step in resolving the ailments of our health care system, both in treating the sick and managing costs, depends on our ability to address the leading cause of illness and fatality in America—aging.

A strong majority of the leading causes of death in the United States today are diseases of the aged body. The conditions leading on the top-ten-killer list compiled by the Centers for Disease Control and Prevention (CDC) are all household

---

1   "The US Burden of Disease Collaborators, The State of US Health, 1990-2016: Burden of Diseases, Injuries, and Risk Factors Among US States," *JAMA* 319, no. 14 (April 2018): 1444–1472.

names among pathologies: heart disease, cancer, chronic respiratory diseases, stroke, Alzheimer's, diabetes, influenza and pneumonia, and kidney disease.[2]

The widespread and devastating impact of these diseases on Americans has led to significant private and governmental efforts, and billions of dollars of investment to find cures and treatments for each condition. Decades of research have helped improve care, medicines, and preventative measures to slow the onset or spread of these diseases, but we still cannot escape their doom.

Fortunately, a growing number of experimental treatments can potentially address the genesis of these fatal conditions.

Brilliant scientists and disruptive entrepreneurs are getting closer to piecing together the biological puzzle that not only answers the question of why we age, but also how we can control it.

Researchers now understand that aging is not only a forward-moving process, but it can also be manipulated—and even reversed. We can age backward.

Research investigating the mechanisms of aging has made considerable progress over the past several decades, aided by the completion of the Human Genome Project and advancements in medical and scientific tools. The aging field is now approaching its tipping point, with the promise of a medical revolution waiting on the other side.

---

2   Center for Disease Control and Prevention, "Leading Causes of Death," accessed March 17, 2017.

But we are not there yet. This excitement—and dreams of dominating on the courts at the ripe age of seventy—must be tempered by the reality of current hurdles blocking Americans from enjoying youth in old age.

To begin, while we have made notable progress in understanding the aging process, significant questions still need to be answered by science. These gaps will hopefully be resolved in time, but certain governmental policies—and a lack of focused resources—are slowing the advancement of new discoveries.

For one, because aging is not classified as a disease, drugs aimed at targeting the mechanisms of aging and not a specific, recognized disease cannot enter the federal clinical trial process as an "aging" drug. This means treatments specifically created to enhance longevity do not currently have a path through the Food and Drug Administration (FDA) and into your pharmacy.

For all Americans to eventually enjoy easy access to these future treatments, the FDA must take steps to classify aging itself as a condition that can be treated. The lack thereof results in significant negative downstream effects that impede the progress of and access to aging drugs.

Without this federal recognition, scientists and entrepreneurs interested in aging are forced to cater research and business pursuits to targeting specific age-related conditions. While this workaround may eventually allow disease-specific drugs that have the added byproduct of increasing longevity to get across the FDA finish line, it could limit the accessibility of the treatment to only those suffering from a specific disease.

And similar to other grant-supported research, the science follows the money. Many aging scientists lack the grant funding necessary to develop and test new aging drugs. While the National Institute on Aging (NIA) has recently seen a strong boost in funding for Alzheimer's research, only a sliver of NIA funds are committed to scientists investigating the actual biological causes of aging.[3,4] Logic would argue that if we could treat aging, individuals would not develop age-related conditions such as Alzheimer's to begin with.

Although interest in aging research has grown in recent years, federal barriers, extensive time horizons, longstanding taboos, and snake-oil salesmanship associated with the aging field have understandably made some financiers hesitant to invest in research or startups.

Overcoming the above obstacles and rebranding the aging industry to reflect the credibility of emerging science will require action from both members of Congress and federal entities. But despite what is at stake—American lives, the US economy, and the solvency of government programs—there has been little movement or interest from government bodies.

Oftentimes, the impetus lawmakers and regulators need are demands from the public. Having worked on Capitol

---

3 "Alzheimer's and Dementia Research: Alzheimer's Research Funding at the NIH," *Alzheimer's Impact Movement*, 2020.

4 "FY 2020 Program Descriptions," *National Institute on Aging*, accessed June 27, 2020.

Hill during a heated debate over health care reform, I am acutely aware of the influence constituents can have over their representatives.

In February 2017, I was hunkered down in Republican Congressman Dave Reichert's Washington State headquarters. As his communications director, I had traveled from Washington, DC to help manage the media and communications response to most of our constituents' disapproval or vocal outrage over the recently introduced Republican health care proposal, the *American Health Care Act* (AHCA). Members of the local police department stood outside of the building's doors, preventing a crowd of several hundred protesters from storming into the building. They had amassed on the street parallel to the office parking lot, holding homemade signs and yelling chants threatening to vote him out of office if he supported the Republican-led health care legislation that had been introduced several months prior in the US House of Representatives. Having grown up in the area, I recognized some of the more animated voices as belonging to my neighbors.

Up until the final morning of the vote on the AHCA in the US House of Representatives, Congressman Reichert's staff did not know whether he would vote "Yay" or "Nay." Despite the tremendous pressure from House leadership and the White House to support the bill, Reichert ultimately decided to vote alongside the majority of his constituents. It would be a "Nay."

With the eventual failure of the AHCA to move through the US Senate, it became clear to me that perhaps more so than any other policy issue, topics surrounding health care can incite political activism.

The roadblocks preventing the development of and Americans' access to longevity treatments deserve the same fervency the fight between the *Affordable Care Act*—"Obamacare"—and the AHCA ignited in years past.

However, regardless of the side you stand on, even the glitziest of insurance plans is unlikely to prevent someone from getting cancer, Alzheimer's, diabetes, or heart disease.

Questions surrounding the future of health care from a policy perspective must still include conversations concerning insurance coverage, but for the sake of our personal and national health, wealth, and wellbeing, we must prioritize the most fundamental unanswered questions about declining health: why do we age and what can we do about it?

Whether you fear ending up like the seventy-five-year-old man imprisoned by the consequences of age or are simply concerned about the looming colossal health care costs of America's aging population, redirecting our health care apparatus to focus on reaching our maximum number of healthy years is in all of our best interest.

The following pages of this book will give you a glimpse of the science that may lengthen the healthspan of your life. Their contents will detail mechanisms scientists have uncovered to return old cells to their youth, treatments that prevent zombie cells from spreading toxins throughout your body, and biotechnology that could allow free-floating livers to grow in your lymph nodes—among many other experimental treatments that may await us in the future. You will hear about the people behind discoveries that have shaped the field of aging research, and about current scientists working on modern cutting-edge treatments that could give your legs the strength to run marathons at age eighty, if you so choose. But you will also learn about the very high, and at times seemingly impenetrable, barriers preventing potential treatments from reaching you, your family, and friends.

It is not a work of science fiction, but I hope this book will compel you to reimagine the longstanding birth-work-death cycle of life, turn your head away from yearning for the past, and, instead, persuade you to look forward with excitement and vigor to the future.

PART 1

THE EVOLUTION OF LIFESPANS

CHAPTER 1

THE NEXT MEDICAL REVOLUTION

———

The black spots on his neck were a certain sign of death.

"No doctor's advice, no medicine could overcome or alleviate this disease," explained the Italian writer Giovanni Boccaccio in the mid-1300s.[5]

Boccaccio was describing the deadly contagion he had witnessed spreading across his city, Florence. By the time the bubonic plague—widely known as the Black Death—had taken its last victim, 60 percent of Florence would be wiped out.[6]

Another Florentine, Agnolo di Tura, compared the layers of dead bodies amassing throughout the city to what could be described as some sort of morbid human lasagna.

---

5   "The Black Death, 1348," *Eyewitness to History*, accessed May 31, 2020.
6   Ibid.

"All the citizens did little else except to carry dead bodies to be buried [...]. At every church they dug deep pits down to the water-table; and thus those who were poor who died during the night were bundled up quickly and thrown into the pit. In the morning when a large number of bodies were found in the pit, they took some earth and shovelled it down on top of them; and later others were placed on top of them and then another layer of earth, just as one makes lasagne with layers of pasta and cheese."[7]

The menacing disease owes its name to the black, puss-filled, blood-oozing boils that surfaced on infected skin. The plague was both efficient and non-discriminatory among mammals. One could lay their head down at night—believing they are in good health—and never rise from their pillow the next morning. Due to its extremely communicable nature, family members were left little choice but to abandon infected loved ones. Mothers and fathers left their children to their inevitable demise, unable to say goodbye. Even those who fled for safety in the countryside found danger in pastures filled with infected farm animals. The plague spread like wildfire, but was more fatal than flames.

In just four years, the Black Death ravaged Europe, killing an estimated 30 to 50 percent of the continent's population.[8] While especially ruthless and wide in its destruction, it was

---

7   Ole J. Benedictow, "The Black Death: The Greatest Catastrophe Ever," *History Today* 3, no. 5 (March 2005). Center for Disease Control and Prevention, "Leading Causes of Death,"

8   DeWitte, Sharon N, "Mortality Risk and Survival in the Aftermath of the Medieval Black Death," *PLOS One* 9, no. 5 (2014).

just one of many plagues, diseases, and other maladies that made most of human life throughout history short and fraught with endless death and suffering.

Today, young professionals entering the workforce largely anticipate living many decades into the future. Those who are wise begin planning for their long retirement at the start of their career. But Americans' expectation of living fifteen-plus years after putting down the shovel from a long day's work is largely a modern phenomenon.

Not too far back, we barely made it to the eligible age to run for the presidency, let alone think about "retirement." In the year 1800, before the advent of modern medicine, there was a 46 percent chance a mother living in America would not see her child live past the age of five.[9] Pick head or tails, the chances of a child surviving were only slightly better than a flip of a coin. That is, of course, if the mother herself survived her infant's birth. And with an average life expectancy of just thirty-seven, even a child that made it past infancy would not spend much time in adulthood. Now, 220 years later, 94.4 percent of children in America make it past the kindergarten playground, and with the current US life expectancy of seventy-six for males and eighty-one for females, those children can expect to live many decades into the future.[10,11]

---

9   Aaron O'Neill, "Child Mortality Rate (Under Five Years Old) in the United States, from 1800 To 2020*," *Statista,* 2019.

10   "United States of America—Under-Five Mortality Rate," *Knoema,* 2018

11   Elizabeth Arias, Jiaquan Xu, and Kenneth D, Kochanek, "United States Life Tables, 2016."

The Black Death deserves its title as mankind's most deadly pandemic, but it was just one of many outbreaks and epidemics that resulted in mass casualties unfathomable by today's standards. In the mid-1800s a cholera outbreak took the lives of some one million persons in Asia, Europe, and North America. The flu pandemic of 1918 wiped out twenty to fifty million, wreaking havoc across the globe.[12] If you and your entire family did not die of a disease of epic or pandemic proportions, you would likely go by tuberculosis, smallpox, measles, chickenpox, cholera, whooping cough, or influenza.

But then, in the nineteenth and twentieth century, humankind made significant advances in science, discovering the existence and role of bacteria and viruses and the importance of sanitation. Quality of life dramatically improved, and life expectancy doubled. And then the discovery of penicillin in 1928 saved countless city dwellers who otherwise would have been taken by the bacteria that permeated industrialized areas. Vaccines led to the near or total eradication of viruses that had fatally infected the young, old, rich, and poor for centuries. Administering a vaccine for the poliovirus in the 1960s alone increased the life expectancy of that generation by more than two decades.[13]

---

12   United States of America—Under-Five Mortality Rate," *Knoema,* 2018.
13   Walter A. Orenstein, and Rafi Ahmed, "Simply Put: Vaccination Saves Lives," *Proceedings of the National Academy of Sciences of the United States of America* 114, no. 16 (2017); "Public Health Initiatives and Life Expectancy: Immunizations," *Regis College,* accessed June 1, 2020.

Advances in modern medicine changed how humans experienced and thought about life. As the late novelist Katherine Dunn wrote, "Prior to penicillin and medical research, death was an everyday occurrence. It was intimate." Dunn was born in 1945, just several years after penicillin began to be produced on a larger scale, and the year Alexander Fleming, Howard Florey, and Ernst Boris Chain won the Nobel Prize in Medicine for their work on the drug.[14]

Penicillin and other new treatments seemed to be medical miracles, but they were not. They were tough problems largely solved by scientists observing specimens under glass in a lab.

Now, for those living in a developed country, catching the flu or getting the chickenpox is more of an inconvenience than a fatal sentence. The gods of death in this new millennium are age-related diseases. Each day, they take the lives of one hundred thousand people across the globe.[15]

Like the flu and plagues of our medieval-era counterparts, we have come to expect death by diseases of old age.

But our expectations are not rules cemented in science. Just as those born in the 1800s would be stunned to see the shelves of a twenty-first-century pharmacy or witness an open-heart surgery, those of us alive today will likely—sooner rather

---

14   Monowar Aziz, and Ping Wang, "What's New in Shock, May 2016?" *Shock (Augusta, Georgia)* 45, no. 5 (2016): 471.

15   Britt Wray, "The Ambitious Quest to Cure Ageing Like a Disease," *BBC*, 2018.

than later—be exposed to new medicines that force us to rethink our perceptions of scientific possibility.

Humankind is at the cusp of another medical revolution. But this time around, the target is not eliminating a bacterium or a virus, the aim is to treat aging itself.

CHAPTER 2

WHAT IS AGING?

———

In January 2013, a group of attendees at the Sundance Film Festival was introduced to an adolescent boy named Sam Berns. In the film *Life According to Sam*, they saw an average kid who was a master Lego builder and a thrill-seeking connoisseur who wanted to ride the fastest and twistiest roller coasters. Like most other boys his age, Sam idolized his local football team, the New England Patriots.

But in truth, Sam was not like most other boys. When his family went on vacation to Disneyland, he cracked several ribs on a ride. And while Sam loved sports, he could never play on a school team, let alone competitively. Sam also did not look like other children his age. The young hands he used to build Legos had protruding knuckles attached to thin fingers that led to yellow-tinted brittle fingernails.[16]

Sam had progeria—a genetic disorder that causes symptoms of advanced aging to occur in children. Although children

———

16   Andrea Nix Fine, and Sean Fine, *Life According to Sam*, 2013; HBO
      documentary films, 2013.

with progeria have the spirit and interests of their peers with the same chronological age, the biological age of their bodies is closer to that of their grandparents. Not long after they start growing hair, they start losing it. Their skin begins to thin and wrinkle, their bones become frail, and they develop arthritis. Then, like the elderly, they eventually succumb to heart failure, stroke, or the overall frailty of their body. Tragically, diseases of aging might take them before many of their healthy friends hit puberty.

Sam passed away on January 10, 2014—almost a year to the day after *Life According to Sam* debuted in Utah. He was seventeen—a very long life for someone with his condition.[17]

When we meet children like Sam or when we visit or remember our grandparents, we can see the visual signs of aging. Grey or balding hair, diminished eyesight and hearing, skin that has lost its elasticity, decreased strength and mobility, and a list of additional ailments that grows longer as the person grows older. Children with progeria age at a much faster rate than the general population. However, the molecular mechanism that causes them to age rapidly is present in all of us, although expressed at a much lower level.

While individuals with progeria are an exception, we typically have an idea about someone's chronological age by observing physical characteristics. We do not need a doctor to tell us when we are or someone we know is old. We instinctively recognize aging when we see it.

---

17 Margalit Fox, "Sam Berns, 17, Public Face of a Rare Illness, Is Dead," *The New York Times*, January 13, 2014.

But what—on a molecular level—is aging? This is the fundamental question science has yet to answer in full, although we know that aging, in simple terms, is an accumulation of cellular damage that impairs our metabolic functions. These breakdowns lead to the physical outer signs of aging we can see and the inner physiological markers we can feel.

A 2013 paper in the journal *Cell* that outlines trademarks of aging put it this way: "Aging is characterized by a progressive loss of physiological integrity, leading to impaired function and increased vulnerability to death. This deterioration is the primary risk factor for major human pathologies, including cancer, diabetes, cardiovascular disorders, and neurodegenerative diseases."

The widely-cited paper then goes on to describe what it diagnosed as the nine hallmarks of aging:

- Genomic instability
- Telomere attrition
- Epigenetic alterations
- Loss of proteostasis
- Deregulated nutrient-sensing
- Mitochondrial dysfunction
- Cellular senescence
- Stem cell exhaustion
- Altered intercellular communication[18]

---

18 Carlos López-Otín, et al., "The Hallmarks of Aging," *Cell* 153, no. 6 (2013); "What Is Aging?" *Life Extension Advocacy Foundation*, accessed June 27, 2020; "What Is Aging?" *Life Extension Advocacy Foundation*, accessed June 27, 2020.

Hallmarks of Aging by McKenzie Deutsch

These terms may read like gibberish now, but they will be explained in full throughout the proceeding pages.

While scientists and gerontologists working in the aging field may put more weight on certain hallmarks over others, it is generally agreed that there are multiple causes of aging with these nine categories as leading contributors.

The consensus is that an individual's chronological age is not the only—and perhaps not the most important—number physicians should consider when determining an individual's health and the likelihood of developing an age-related disease. The more relevant data point is an individual's *biological* age.

Our biological age is impacted by a variety of lifestyle factors, including diet, sun exposure, exercise levels, alcohol consumption, and genes. Excluding the influence of genetics, an individual's habits may cause their biological age to be higher or lower than their chronological age.[19]

A forty-year-old who spent decades smoking cigarettes, lying bare-skinned on a beach, and eating chicken wings in the shadow of a big-screen TV will likely have a biological age greater than their birth certificate would indicate. On the other hand, someone who grew up eating leafy greens, wearing sunscreen, and exercising regularly may very well be younger biologically than their chronological age. Genetic advantages or disadvantages passed down by parents, such as a predisposition for cardiovascular disease, also influence an individual's biological age. In short, our biological age is a combination of lifestyle, genetics, and our number of rotations around the sun.

Unlike our fixed chronological age, we have the power to manipulate and even move the minute hand backward on our biological clock.

We have likely all seen someone "grow" younger by observing changes in their external appearance, e.g., the shiny hair of the neighbor who replaced processed foods with whole foods, the glowing skin of the colleague who quit smoking or

---

19   S. Michal Jazwinski, et al., "Examination of the Dimensions of Biological Age," *Frontiers in Genetics* 10 (2019): 263.

drinking, or perhaps the slimmer waist of the former serial Netflix viewer who lost weight while training for a marathon.

Although their improved health and a more youthful appearance are visual biological age signs both a doctor and layperson can recognize, these signals do not give us the full physiological picture of an individual's overall health and their true biological age.

But scientists are working on solutions to that problem. One such tool is bio-mathematician Steve Horvath's epigenetic clock. Dr. Horvath's clock can predict an individual's age with compelling accuracy. By measuring DNA methylation—a type of genetic "rust"—the clock estimates an individual's age. When looking at tissue samples from a broad spectrum of specimens taken from throughout the body, the clock had a median error of 3.6 years. It is even more accurate when looking at samples from certain tissues in particular with 2.7 years of accuracy from saliva, 1.9 years from some white blood cells, and only 1.5 years with tissue taken from the brain cortex.[20]

Dr. Horvath's clock was, in part, a response to a pact he made decades earlier in Germany.

As a teenager, he and his twin brother, along with their mutual friend, founded the Gilgamesh Project. The genesis of the name stemmed from the Mesopotamian poem, the *Epic of Gilgamesh*, in which the legendary Sumerian king

---

20　W. Wayt, Gibbs, "Biomarkers and Ageing: The Clock-Watcher," *Nature* 508, no. 7495 (2014): 168-170.

sets out on a perilous journey to restore his youth and cure disease through the powers of a mythical plant.

Taking inspiration from Gilgamesh, young Dr. Horvath and fellow Gilgamesh Project members sought to pursue their own epic journeys to find the fountain of youth, and met regularly to consider contemporary cures to the ailments of old age.

"At some point, we realized that this was one of the central problems of human existence: our short lives," he recounted to the outlet OneZero.[21]

The teenage boys wondered if modern science could produce a real version of the rejuvenating plant Gilgamesh searched for. The three of them vowed to dedicate their careers to doing so.

The chase for a tangible elixir of life is still on, and Dr. Horvath continues to improve his calculators to fulfill his boyhood pact. In early 2019, he released a newer, more advanced clock that is 18 percent more accurate than chronological age at predicting an individual's lifespan, and 14 percent more accurate than other epigenetic biomarkers. Fittingly, in tribute to the Grim Reaper, it is called the "GrimAge."[22]

Inventions such as the GrimAge, and the increasing number of other "clocks" that measure various age-related biomarkers,

---

21 Daniel Kolitz, "A New Test Predicts When You'll Die (Give or Take a Few Years)," *Onezero*, January 23, 2019.

22 Ake T. Luke, Austin Quach, James G. Wilson, Alex P. Reiner, et al., "DNA Methylation GrimAge Strongly Predicts Lifespan and Healthspan," *Aging (Albany NY)* 11, no. 2 (2019): 303.

have been useful tools for aging researchers as they work to test the effectiveness of experimental treatments.

However, Dr. Horvath's clock and similar technologies are not accepted testing mechanisms for proving a treatment's worth during the FDA's clinical trial system. The lack of an approved testing standard for aging drugs is just one of the steep—but not insurmountable—roadblocks preventing treatments aimed at extending your number of healthy years from reaching your pharmacy.

So what are the leading roadblocks to progress? And is there a path forward?

CHAPTER 3

ROADBLOCKS TO PROGRESS AND THE PATH FORWARD

THE GOVERNMENT IS A PIVOTAL PLAYER IN BIOMEDICAL INNOVATION

Scalpels, forceps, needles, and scissors—these were tools most often used by doctors caring for cancer patients prior to modern chemotherapy treatments. Procedures were brutal and bloody, and reprieve from the metastasizing disease was usually short-lived.

But that changed in 1956 when doctors at the National Cancer Institute (NCI), Roy Hertz and Min C. Li, published their research on a chemotherapy drug targeting gestational choriocarcinoma, a highly fatal cancer that forms in the placenta of pregnant women. Through their work supported by NCI, they discovered that the drug methotrexate could save women from the deadly malignant tumor that had previously ended the lives of almost all of those with the disease. This was the first time a chemotherapy drug had proven capable of targeting solid tumors. By 1972, 90 percent of women treated with both methotrexate and actinomycin-D were cured of a cancer that, in the past, would have almost surely been fatal.

Dr. Hertz's and Dr. Li's findings paved the way for future advancements in treatments that have now made many cancers curable. Their research is just one example of the litany of life-saving discoveries that have resulted from the support of the National Institutes of Health (NIH).[23]

There is no question that grants from the NIH have been fundamental to America's position as a world leader in biomedical research. In a study where researchers reviewed the top one hundred most commonly prescribed drugs in the US, they found 93 percent received funding from the NIH. Newer drugs have benefited even more. Of the drugs that made it through the FDA's approval process between 2010 and 2016, 97 percent were supported by NIH grants.[24]

Each year, the NIH invests roughly $39.2 billion into medical research. Over 80 percent of this amount is used to fund nearly fifty thousand grants, benefiting more than three hundred thousand researchers at more than twenty-five hundred universities, medical schools, and research institutions throughout the world. Another 10 percent of the NIH's budget is distributed internally, funding research conducted by

---

23   Eric Pace, "Roy Hertz, 93, Discoverer of a Cancer Treatment," *The New York Times*, 2002.

24   Dmitry Kaminskiy, et al., "Metabesity and Longevity USA Special Case Study," *Aging Analytics Agency*, 2019.

nearly six thousand scientists working in its laboratories.[25] As of 2019, 156 Nobel Laureates have received funding from the NIH.[26]

America is the envy of the world when it comes to biomedical research and innovation. However, overall funding for the NIH has trended downward since 2003, dropping by 11 percent in real dollars as of 2018. This has, in turn, impacted researchers' access to grants. In 2003, around 30 percent of grant proposals received funding. By 2015, that number had declined to only 15 percent. At the same time, global competitors, including China, have ramped up their focus on biomedical research.[27]

Still, the research opportunities available in the States are a large part of the reason the US is home to many of the world's leading scientists, hospitals, research organizations, and institutes of higher education. Both the nation's human talent and investment in the sciences have led to the countless medicines and treatments that have made life in America—and around the world—longer, healthier, and happier.

WHERE THE MONEY GOES AND HOW IT IS DISTRIBUTED

The NIH's budget, and thus the budget of its twenty-seven institutes and centers, is determined by the US House and

25 Jim Dryden-Wustl, "NIH Funding Cuts Could Paralyze Drug Development," *Futurity*, November 19, 2017.

26 National Health Institute, "Nobel Laureates," October 15, 2019.

27 Kaminskiy, "Metabesity and Longevity USA Special Case Study," *Aging Analytics Agency*, 2019.

Senate. Members sitting on the budget and appropriations committees, in part, determine funding levels by considering the sitting president's budget proposal. When drafting the budget submitted to Congress, the president takes into account requested funding levels from the various government bodies, including the NIH. To make a strong case for its funding requests, the NIH and its subset of branches need to make a compelling argument defending the merits of its research and areas of biomedicine worthy of further exploration.

Congress must then agree on and pass budget and appropriations bills. However, once the NIH receives its appropriated funds, its own leadership largely determines where the dollars are directed.

This includes funds distributed within the National Institute on Aging (NIA). Established in 1974, the NIA is the primary research body investigating the underlying mechanisms of aging, as well as the diseases and conditions associated with old age. It is also the principal branch tasked with finding a treatment for Alzheimer's disease. Despite aging being the greatest factor in many of America's most fatal diseases, it receives little attention from the government. Out of the total NIH budget, the department within the NIA researching the biology of aging receives less than 1 percent of the total lump sum of medical research dollars.

Instead, much of the money allocated to the NIA is directed toward the research of age-related conditions. In 2018, for example, Congress appropriated $3.5 billion in additional grant funds to the NIA. While a cause for celebration within the institute, only a slim 3 percent of the dollars was directed to the department studying the biology of aging. The vast majority was instead directed toward Alzheimer's research.

While Alzheimer's has devastated countless families, and research looking into treatments is worthy of our greatest scientific minds, finding a cure would not actually significantly extend an individual's life. It is estimated that curing Alzheimer's would only increase an individual lifespan by nineteen days.[28]

The lopsided funding priorities have not escaped the attention of leading aging researchers. Renowned biologist and aging researcher Leonard Hayflick, PhD, among others, have been openly critical of the NIA's focus on researching age-related diseases, rather than aging itself.

"It's erroneous to believe that understanding diseases associated with old age will give us insight into the basic mechanisms of aging," Dr. Hayflick said in an interview with *The Scientist*. "The resolution tomorrow of Alzheimer's will not advance our knowledge of the fundamental biology of aging in the same way that the resolution of polio did not advance our understanding of child development."[29]

Cancer researchers also receive a disproportionate amount of government resources. As Harvard geneticist David Sinclair, PhD, lamented, "Aging disables 93 percent of people over the

28 Ibid.
29 Steven Benowitz, "Does NIA Spend Too Much on Alzheimer's?" *The Scientist*, February 19, 1996.

age of fifty, but in 2018 the NIH spent on aging less than a tenth of what was spent on cancer research."[30]

While scientists studying and developing aging treatments remain primarily reliant on government grants, there has been an increasing interest in longevity drugs among the tech and investor community. Tech titans—including Google's Calico project, businessmen Jeff Bezos and Peter Thiel, and philanthropists such as Jim Melon—have either started their own ventures or poured cash into aging startups.

Researchers and entrepreneurs now have opportunities to compete for private dollars, but this pool of money is still limited and often comes with strings. Most financiers, unsurprisingly, seek to make a return on their investment. While the potential payoff of a successful longevity drug would be tremendous, many experimental drug candidates are still in early areas of exploration, and even if a drug earns the green light to enter the FDA's clinical trial process, working its way through the system could take well over a decade—if it is successful. In total, only about 12 percent of all drugs in development eventually win approval from the FDA.[31]

Considering those realities, how does a researcher or entrepreneur make a case to a venture firm interested in turning a profit in the near future? For firms and individuals that do decide to put down money, it is most often

---

30 David Sinclair, *Lifespan: Why We Age—and Why We Don't Have To* (New York: Atria Publishing Group, 2019).

31 Thomas Sullivan, "A Tough Road: Cost to Develop One New Drug Is $2.6 Billion; Approval Rate for Drugs Entering Clinical Development Is Less Than 12%," *Policy & Medicine*, 2019.

on experimental drugs already far along in their development, not the actual research necessary to find potential drug candidates or to answer lingering questions about mechanisms of aging.

There are some efforts to crowdsource funds, especially for particularly novel or high-risk studies. The educational non-profit organization, Life Extension Advocacy Fund (LEAF), has fully funded aging research projects by crowdsourcing donations through its website.[32] However, while important, these efforts will not even begin to cover the costs to perform all of the necessary avenues of aging research and the average $19 million it takes to move a potential treatment through to Phase III clinical trials.[33]

The moral of the story has always been—and will likely continue to be—the research follows the money.

Without adequate allocation of funds for research grants investigating the underlying biological causes of aging, few scientists will have the opportunity to take these fundamental questions to the lab. And many of the brightest minds emerging from universities in the States and around the globe will make the seemingly wise career decision of pursuing questions in science where there are dollars already available to support their quest for answers.

---

32 "Discover Campaigns," *Life Extension Advocacy Foundation*, accessed June 27, 2020.

33 "Thomas J. Moore, "Estimated Costs of Pivotal Trials for Novel Therapeutic Agents Approved by the US Food and Drug Administration, 2015-2016," *JAMA Internal Medicine* 178, no. 11 (2018): 1451-1457.

AGING AS A TREATABLE CONDITION

As mentioned previously, to enter the FDA clinical trial process, a potential drug candidate must target a recognized disease or condition with defining qualities that have been agreed to by regulators. Aging is not categorized as either by the FDA, and to reiterate, a treatment labeled as an "aging" drug cannot currently enter clinical trials.

Instead, scientists tackling one or multiple of the nine hallmarks of aging—be it epigenetic alterations or senescent cells—must cater their research and studies toward combating one of the age-related diseases recognized by regulatory bodies.

America is not an outlier in this regard. Currently, no country considers aging itself a disease or a treatable condition. However, progress was made in 2018 when the World Health Organization (WHO) included the extension code "Ageing-related" in a draft version of its updated International Classification of Diseases (ICD). "Ageing-related," as defined by the WHO, means "caused by pathological processes which persistently lead to the loss of organism's adaptation and progress in older ages."[34]

Although the WHO is not an American regulatory body, the ICD does have influence both over the US and international drug regulatory systems. Tying a potential drug or therapy to an ICD-recognized disease is almost always a necessary prerequisite to enter the FDA's clinical trial process.

---

34 "ICD-11 for Mortality and Morbidity Statistics," International World Health Organization, 2018.

But the inclusion of a code defining the term "ageing-related" is not a sign of the WHO's acceptance of aging as a disease. Instead, it is a recognition that pathologies can be, in part, a result of the aged body.

Whether or not aging should be officially categorized as a disease is a contentious topic of debate among aging researchers and those interested in the development of aging drugs.

Some, including Harvard's Dr. Sinclair, believe that the qualifications preventing aging from meeting the definition of a disease are arbitrary.

"Currently, the medical definition of a disease is something that causes a dysfunction or disability that happens to less than half of the population," he explains in an interview with LEAF.

"Of course, aging happens to most of the population now, but I think that having a cut-off at 50 percent is arbitrary. Something that causes a decline in functionality and eventual death should be worked on just as vigorously as something that only affects a minority of people," Dr. Sinclair states.[35]

Others, including gerontologists Cathal McCrory and Rose Anne Kenny of Trinity College Dublin, believe defining aging as a disease will create a stigma around the elderly who are already suffering from the societal consequences of "ageism."

---

35   Steve Hill, "David Sinclair on NMN and Epigenetics," *Life Extension Advocacy Foundation*, September 10, 2019.

"We feel that labeling ageing as a disease serves to reinforce ageist stereotypes and risks legitimizing insidious prejudice and discrimination of older people based on age. A growing body of research indicates that such prejudice affects not just psychological health but also physical function, wellbeing, and mortality," they wrote in the medical journal *The Lancet*.[36]

Regardless of semantics revolving around terminologies, determining whether aging is a disease, as is cancer or Alzheimer's, is less important than determining its classification as something that can be treated with prescription medication or a medical procedure. Without the recognition that it *is* treatable, drugs or treatments labeled as remedies for aging will not be welcomed by the FDA.

That is why although the WHO's inclusion of "ageing-related" in the ICD is helpful, it will not create the regulatory shift necessary to make writing prescriptions for aging drugs commonplace in doctor's offices.

"The real change will come when a leading country says that aging is a disease that can have a medicine approved for treatment," Dr. Sinclair says.

He elaborates: "Right now, because aging is not a condition that's agreed upon by any regulator, drugs that may slow or reverse aging, and perhaps extend lifespan, healthy lifespan, for many years, doctors are very hesitant to prescribe those medicines. They follow the rule book."[37]

---

36   Rose Anne Kenny and Cathal McCrory, "Rebuking the Concept of Ageing as a Disease," *The Lancet* 6, no. 10 (2018): 768.

37   Hill, "David Sinclair on NMN and Epigenetics."

METFORMIN AND THE POTENTIAL
FOR A PATH FORWARD

One drug may carve a path to make an exception to this rule—and it has already been prescribed to more than 120 million people. Metformin, or "glucose eater," is now one of the world's most widely prescribed diabetes drugs, earning a place on the WHO's "Model List of Essential Medicines."[38,39] The white, circular or oval-shaped pill finds its origins in the plant *Galega officinalis*, more widely referred to as goat's rue, French lilac, Italian fitch, or professor-weed. Today, if in the British countryside or grassy plains of Europe, you may not give the long-stemmed, purple, white, or blue-flowered plant a second glance. One might even mistake it for a roadside weed. However, for centuries, this herb has served as a common remedy in folk medicine.

Since the Middle Ages, the plant has been used as a traditional herbal treatment for the flu, the plague, snake bites, and symptoms of diabetes. Tea made from its leaves was even used to treat a medieval lady or gentleman suffering from irregular, infrequent urination. In the seventeenth century, scientific and medical minds first began to describe the blood-glucose-lowering properties of goat's rue, but it was unclear which ingredients in the plant's extract were responsible for its metabolic effect on the body.

It was later discovered that guanidine was the mystery compound within the plant that caused blood glucose levels to lower. The problem was that when taken on its own, guanidine

---

38   Clifford J. Bailey, "Metformin: Historical Overview," *Diabetologia* 60, no. 9 (2017): 1566-1576.

39   "WHO Model List of Essential Medicines," *The World Health Organization*, 2015.

proved to be highly toxic, even deadly. Chemists in the early 1920s discovered that the compound's adverse effects could be resolved in the lab. When bonded with another guanidine, creating a biguanide, the new, synthesized compound proved to be more tolerable on the body. Metformin proved itself to be the safest of the biguanides and eventually found its way to clinical development in France in the 1950s.

Americans would have to wait until 1994 for the glucose eater to makes its way through the FDA. Once metformin became available through a doctor's office visit, patients diagnosed with type 2 diabetes soon found the medication to be effective in its treatment of diabetic symptoms without having the unwanted side effect of weight gain (typical of many other diabetes drugs on the market). In fact, studies showed that the positive impacts of metformin went beyond treating the symptoms of type 2 diabetes. The most famous of these investigations was the United Kingdom Prospective Diabetes Study. For twenty years—1977 to 1997—researchers followed 3,867 patients with type 2 diabetes on a variety of diabetes drugs. Patients given metformin had drawn the lucky straw; the drug emerged as the clear winner. Diabetics on metformin lived longer and had a lower risk of heart disease when compared to individuals taking insulin or sulfonylureas to maintain the same blood glucose levels. The study, anecdotal results, and metformin's patent expiration in 2002—now making it one of the least expensive available drugs—have all contributed to its continuous rise in popularity among doctors and patients.[40]

---

40 Clifford J. Bailey, "Metformin: Historical Overview," *Diabetologia* 60, no. 9 (2017) 1566-1576; Tomislav Meštrović, "Metformin History," *News Medical Life Sciences,* 2018.

Its reputation as an old, reliable, and safe drug that has already been shown to delay age-related diseases was a leading factor in the decision of Nir Barzilai, MD, of the Albert Einstein College of Medicine, to lobby the FDA to use metformin as the first drug to undergo clinical trials with the target goal of increasing healthspan—the amount of time spent without developing an age-related disease.

"Aging drives diseases and targeting aging is a feasible approach that regulators have not yet digested. Metformin is an example of a drug that targets the biology of aging," said Dr. Barzilai in a news release.[41]

The Targeting Aging with Metformin (TAME) study is unlike traditional clinical trials where researchers predict an experimental drug will treat a specific disease. Instead, TAME aims to prove that using metformin will delay the onset of a basket of age-related diseases, including cardio-vascular disease, stroke, diabetes, cancer, cognitive decline, and death. If successful, results will show that seniors without diabetes taking metformin will spend several years disease-free before developing a chronic condition, unlike their peers not on the drug. To prove this theory, trials will follow three thousand individuals between the ages of sixty-five and seventy-nine over the course of three years. It will measure the health outcomes of those taking metformin versus those on a placebo pill.[42]

---

41   "Dr. Nir Barzilai to Present at the 6th Aging Research for Drug Discovery Forum in Basel," *Insilico Medicine*, 2019.

42   Hartmut H. Glossmann, "Metformin and Aging: A Review," *Gerontology* 65, no. 6 (2016): 581-590.

In part, the idea behind this approach was to avoid the difficult task of attempting to define "aging" in a way that could be measured in a clinical setting. The FDA has shown a reluctance to use biomarkers—such as changes in hormone levels or tools such as the Horvath clock—as indications of a treatment's ability to control health risks tied to aging. Instead, for now, regulators see more tangible endpoints, such as frailty or disease, as a way forward to test longevity drugs.

Proving metformin's efficacy as a healthspan treatment is not the only objective of the trial. The hope is TAME will create a clinical trial design that could be replicated by other groups hoping to move an aging drug through regulators and into doctors' offices.

"The significance of the TAME trial is its pioneering engagement with the FDA on how clinical trials that target aging may be approached," explains Dr. Barzilai and members of the TAME team in the journal *Public Policy & Aging Report*.

They elaborate: "The key to a clinical trial targeting aging biology is that its efficacy is not based on outcomes related to a single disease, but instead on a composite endpoint of multiple age-related diseases that share common metabolic drivers and close associations with increasing age.

"The TAME trial could be the first major step toward attaining approval for extending healthspan, and could encourage the development of new, more robust drugs for this indication."[43]

---

43   G. Alexander, Fleming, "A Regulatory Pathway for Medicines That Target Aging," *Public Policy & Aging Report* 29 no. 4 (2019): 128-133.

At the time of writing, the TAME trial is still short of funding necessary to begin the study. While the expiration of metformin's patent made it one of the most affordable available prescriptions for diabetes, its designation as a generic drug also means a pharmaceutical company or a potential investor who funded the trials would not make a profit if it passed through the FDA and succeeded on the market as a drug that slows the aging process. The TAME team will need to rely, in part, on individuals driven by a return on their time, not a monetary investment. Altogether, the trial is expected to cost $75 million.[44]

The research and experimental drugs detailed throughout the following pages are just some of the treatments that could potentially be impacted by clinical trial frameworks outlined by the TAME study. But until the FDA agrees on a path forward, the current longevity drugs entering clinical trials will only be candidates for a specific disease or condition—leaving countless seniors without a cabinet of potentially preventative treatment options and inhibiting individuals who want to take steps now to extend their healthspan and avert later-life diseases.

Despite the current monetary hurdle, Dr. Barzilai is optimistic about the tremendous societal benefits developing a successful framework to test longevity drugs will create: "Everyone knows there is a biology of aging. For some reason, they think they can't do anything about it. That is a mistake. You can intervene in aging, even late in aging. Our lives are going to change when we have the regulatory pathway to do that."[45]

---

44 Aubrey de Grey, "TAME: A Genuinely Good Use of 75 Million Dollars," *Rejuvenation Research* 22, no. 5 (2019): 375-376.

45 Regina Schaffer, "Metformin May Hold Anti-Aging Promise to Increase 'Health Span,'" *Healio*, 2020.

Experimental drugs and treatments that have the potential to tackle the nine hallmarks of aging are waiting for that pathway to be carved. In the following chapters, you will learn about some of these pioneering approaches to improving our health and the stories of the scientists, entrepreneurs, philanthropists, and activists behind their creation.

CHAPTER 4

A CELL IN A PETRI DISH

———

In May 1912, Alexis Carrel, a surgeon, biologist, and Nobel Laureate, challenged existing theories on aging by announcing to the world that our cells, when separated from our body and cultured in a dish, could potentially live on indefinitely. They were, in theory, immortal. In a paper published by the prestigious science journal *The Journal of Experimental Medicine*, he wrote that it is "conceivable that the length of the life of a tissue outside of the organism could exceed greatly its normal duration in the body, because elemental death might be postponed indefinitely by a proper artificial nutrition."[46]

Several months prior, Dr. Carrel had removed a piece of a still-beating heart from a chick embryo that had been separated from its egg. The tissue was then cultured in a dish in Dr. Carrel's lab and fed nutrient-rich plasma.

---

46   Alexis Carrel, "On the Permanent Life of Tissues Outside of the Organism," *Journal of Experimental Medicine* 15, no. 5 (1912): 516-528.

Dr. Carrel and his team watched as the heart tissue cells sitting in the protected glass of the petri dish continued to multiply and thrive, far surpassing the lifespan of an average chicken. This contradicted the standing scientific thinking at the time, which contended cells had a programmed cycle that ended in death within a specific, preordained time frame. According to Dr. Carrel, his experiment proved it is not an internal clock within our cells that causes our cells—and thus all of us—to die, but it is the impact outside factors have on the health of our cells.[47]

Dr. Carrel, already a darling of the scientific world and not one to shy away from the limelight, rose to superstardom with his findings. Many thereafter dared to dream about the potential limitlessness of human life. In September 1935, twenty-three years after the initial experiment, the still-living chicken heart continued to capture the curiosity and imagination of the American public, and *TIME* magazine put Dr. Carrel on its front cover.[48] He gave the press periodic updates on the health of the heart culture and invited reporters tso tour his lab, which he had painted black from ceiling to floor in the erroneous belief the dark color would prevent contamination.

A 1938 edition of *TIME* magazine, where he again appeared on the cover, detailed the layout of his strange black lab. The reporter wrote, "A secluded labyrinth of black, dustless, germless laboratories zigzags across the top floor of the main building of the Rockefeller Institute for Medical Research in

47 Hill, "David Sinclair on NMN and Epigenetics,"
48 "Medicine: Carrel's Man," *TIME*, 1935.

Manhattan. Black are the floors, black the furniture, dark grey the windowless walls, shadowless the bleak illumination that comes through the skylights." Keeping on brand, scientists in Dr. Carrel's lab dressed in black lab coats.[49]

Finally, in the 1940s after Dr. Carrel's death, the eternal chicken heart culture met its demise when his assistant discarded its remains in the trash. Over the decades, other scientists had tried—unsuccessfully—to replicate Dr. Carrel's experiment. Unwilling to challenge a man of such notoriety, these scientists largely blamed their failure to achieve the same results on their own perceived inadequacies. Some blamed deviance in results on contamination, others on their lack of skill.[50]

Dr. Carrel's theory of the immortal cell persisted until one day in the early 1960s when young cell biologist Leonard Hayflick thought he had made a mistake while working in a small lab in Philadelphia's Wistar Institute. Dr. Hayflick was using cells from human tissue as part of his research into the potential relationship between viruses and some cancers. To his surprise and confusion, he noticed that a sample of the cultured cells was acting strange. The cells had stopped dividing—a process of cell reproduction called mitosis. A few weeks later, he noticed the same phenomena with cultures made from separate human tissue cells. After looking through his notes, Dr. Hayflick realized that the cell cultures that ceased mitosis were older than the other cell cultures that continued to reproduce.

---

49 "Medicine: Men in Black," *TIME*, 1938.
50 John Rasko, "What Pushes Scientists to Lie? The Disturbing but Familiar Story of Haruko Obokata," *The Guardian*, 2015.

The cells' behavior defied the dogma of the 'immortal human cell' that had been cemented over the past sixty years. To prove himself right—or wrong—he repeated the experiment several additional times. The results were clear— human cells, even in the protection of a lab dish, were mere mortals.

Dr. Hayflick's findings made several significant contributions to scientific thinking and the study of aging. First, contrary to Dr. Carrel's claims, unlike cancerous cells, which continued to proliferate, normal human cells were not immortal. Their death was not caused solely by outside factors, such as radiation or stress. Instead, cells seemed to have a finite lifespan, and their death was caused by events largely happening within the cell. Second, cells reproduce at slower rates as they age and eventually stop dividing altogether when they reach the senescent—inactive—stage. He observed that within human cells, it took roughly fifty to seventy divisions before cell senescence occurred. This would later become known as the "Hayflick limit." Dr. Hayflick's discovery also distinguished healthy human cells from cancerous cells, which truly were immortal. This would prove to be an important development in cancer research.[51]

How did the myth of human cell immortality persist for six decades? And was Dr. Carrel's experiment a complete fraud or were his stated conclusions an honest mistake? Some say Dr. Carrel and his laboratory assistants pulled off one of the biggest hoaxes in the history of science. Others say that it may have been the result of accidentally putting live chick cells in

---

51   Jordanna Cepelewicz, "Ingenious: Leonard Hayflick," *Nautilus*, 2016.

the liquid used as a medium and nutrition for the cultured cells, which could have re-seeded the cultured cells.[52]

While Dr. Hayflick's discovery was an example of the importance of questioning and testing accepted science, the response to his findings was an example of the stubborn and perhaps self-interested mentality that existed among some leading members of the scientific community. Due to the nature of his findings, Dr. Hayflick thought it would be fitting to send his paper to the same journal in which Dr. Carrel had published his chicken heart experiment sixty years prior.

Upon receiving the paper, the *Journal of Experimental Medicine* responded, "Anyone working in tissue culture knows that given the right milieu, in vitro normal cells are immortal." The rejection letter's author, Dr. Francis Peyton Rous, who would later receive a Nobel Prize in Medicine for his research on the connection between viruses and certain types of cancer, also called Dr. Hayflick's suggestion that there was a relationship between cellular senescence and aging "notably rash."[53]

Fortunately for Dr. Hayflick—and for humankind—the journal *Experimental Cell Research* published the paper without hesitation or revision. Today, Dr. Hayflick's "The serial cultivation of human diploid cell strains" is one of the most-cited scientific papers of all time.[54] However, after its

---

52 Rasko, "What Pushes Scientists to Lie?"

53 Cepelewicz, "Ingenious: Leonard Hayflick,"; "Peyton Rous Biographical," *The Nobel Prize Foundation*, accessed June 3, 2020.

54 L. Hayflick, "The Serial Cultivation of Human Diploid Cell Strains," *Experimental Cell Research* 25, no. 3 (1961): 585-621.

initial publication in 1961 the science community was still reluctant to accept Hayflick's findings. To win over his peers, science would need to go beyond proving that human cells age at a particular rate. Researchers would need to begin to demonstrate the intracellular mechanisms that help explain why our cells age and why they stop dividing.

It would take over a decade, but scientists would eventually discover part of that question could be answered by observing the shortening of protective caps at the end of our chromosomes: telomeres.

PART 2

THE HALLMARKS OF AGING

CHAPTER 5

TELOMERE ATTRITION

———

Telomeres are protective caps at the end of our chromosomes. With each cell division, telomeres become shorter in length, eventually becoming so short that cells cease to divide and enter a state of senescence.

In 1971, an ocean away from Dr. Leonard Hayflick's lab in Philadelphia, a theoretical biologist living in what was then the Soviet Union learned of Hayflick's discovery while attending a lecture at Moscow University. This was the second time Alexey Olovnikov heard about the Hayflick limit while attending a university class, but the first time he paid attention. It now struck him that the Hayflick limit posed a "giant, exciting, captivating mystery" about cellular aging.

Why did cells seem to have a limit on the number of times they could divide, and why when they reached that number did they become senescent? How can cells even have an internal counting system? These questions rattled his mind as he left the lecture theater and made his way to a subway station in Moscow.

Olovnikov remembers this day in detail.

"I was simply thunderstruck by the novelty and beauty of the Hayflick limit. I thought about this as I returned home from University and walked along the quiet Moscow streets that were paved with gold-colored leaves on that early evening in late fall as I made my way to the subway station," he recalls.[55]

He eventually reached the subway station, continuing to ponder what internal cellular mechanism resulted in the Hayflick limit as he stood on the noisy platform. He watched as the rumbling train moved toward his stop and observed how the passengers hurried on and off on their way to their destination.

And then the spark of genius hit him.

He visualized the train as though it were a strand of replicating DNA. If the engine of the train was tasked with replicating the track—the DNA—would not be replicated since it would be hidden under the engine.

He called this the theory of "marginotomy"—the trimming of ends. It later became known as the "telomere hypothesis."

TELOMERES AND DNA

Several years later, and unaware of Olovnikov's theory, Elizabeth Blackburn, PhD, was using the single-celled

---

55   Michael D. West, "Dr. Alexey Olovnikov Explains His Conception of the Telomere Hypothesis of Cell Aging," 2017, Video.

pond-dwelling creature, *Tetrahymena thermophila*, to study chromosomes while working on her post doctorate at Yale University. Dr. Blackburn did not discover telomeres, but during her time at Yale she worked with her mentor Joseph Gall, PhD, to begin to uncover a clearer picture of the molecular biology of telomeres and the role they play in protecting chromosomes.[56]

Telomeres are part of our DNA's structure. They sit at each end of DNA strands—where chromosomes are located—and protect the critical genetic information these coiled, thread-like structures contain. The genetic information held in our DNA is the maestro of our bodily functions. Among countless other activities, it directs our bodies to convert food to energy, remove waste, and protect us against foreign invaders attempting to infect our bodies with disease.[57]

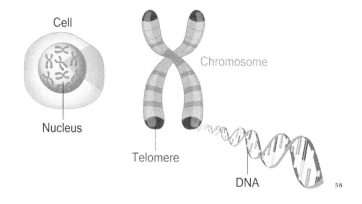

Cell

Chromosome

Nucleus

Telomere

DNA

58

---

56 "Elizabeth Blackburn: Nobel Prize in Physiology or Medicine 2009," *The Nobel Prize Foundation*.

57 Clare O'Connor, "Telomeres of Human Chromosomes," *Nature*, 2008.

58 Fancy Tapis, *Telomeres Are Protective Caps on the End of Chromosomes, Cell, Chromosome and DNA Vector Illustration*, Image.

At the time, Dr. Blackburn did not realize the important influence telomeres had in the aging process. However, her work helped scientists understand some of the basic biology of telomeres, which led to important future observations by other scientists.

One such discovery was that telomeres become shorter through each cell division, which decreases their ability to protect the information stored in our DNA over time.

A common analogy used to illustrate the relationship between telomeres and chromosomes is a shoelace and the aglets at its ends. Just as the plastic aglet at each tip of a shoelace prevents the thread's fibers from unraveling, telomeres protect the integrity of the genetic material housed in chromosomes. However, telomeres face the same fate as well-used shoelaces. With each trail we hike, road we cross, and stair we climb, we put stress on our shoelaces and eventually they begin to fray.

Similarly, with each cell division, telomeres grow shorter until, eventually, they can no longer do their job of protecting the integrity of genetic material and preventing our DNA from unraveling.

TELOMERE

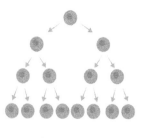

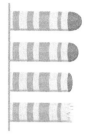

Cells Divide   Telomeres Shorten ₅₉

Scientists, including Dr. Howard Cooke, Dr. Cal Harley, and Dr. Carol Greider published papers showing a reduction in telomere length with each cellular division.[60,61] It would eventually be understood that once telomere length dwindled to a certain critical point, the cell would cease to divide; it would reach the Hayflick limit and become senescent.

With its vital duty maintaining the integrity of our DNA and allowing for the production of new sister cells, a healthy telomere length is essential to our overall well-being and our body's ability to function at a high level. However, as they decrease in size with each division, the likelihood for cellular mutation increases and they become closer to reaching an inactive, senescent state. For

59 Fancy Tapis, *Cells Divide—Telomeres Shorten,* Image.
60 H.J. Cooke, "Variability at the Telomeres of the Human X/Y Pseudoautosomal Region," *Cold Spring Harbor Symposia on Quantitative Biology* 51, no. 0 (1986): 213–219
61 Calvin B. Harley, "Telomeres Shorten During Ageing of Human Fibroblasts," *Nature* 345, no. 6274 (1990): 458–460.

this reason, telomere attrition is considered a significant hallmark of aging.[62]

But in 1984, Dr. Blackburn and her mentee, Dr. Carol Greider, believed they may have found an antidote to telomere shortening. Together, they discovered telomerase—an enzyme that produces telomeres' DNA and maintains and stimulates their growth. While their research was again focused on the pond organism *Tetrahymena thermophila,* the discovery left scientists interested in the study of aging with profound questions.[63] If human telomerase could be located and cloned, could the length of our telomeres be protected and could our shortened telomeres be regrown? What impact would that have on the human aging process?

THE RACE TO FIND HUMAN TELOMERASE

It was the early 1990s and Michael D. West had made the huge and, according to many of his peers, unwise decision of founding a biotech company as a third-year medical student. He had read papers published on telomeres and telomerase, including those by Dr. Greider and Dr. Harley, and was familiar with Olovnikov's telomere hypothesis.

There were, of course, still many unanswered questions about the role of telomeres and telomerase in human aging. He figured, but mostly suspected, that if he could locate the genetic sequence for telomerase in human cells— the enzyme that lengthens telomeres—then the secret to

---

62 López-Otín, 6.

63 "Elizabeth Blackburn: Nobel Prize in Physiology or Medicine 2009," *The Nobel Prize Foundation.*

unlocking the fountain of youth could be hiding in plain sight, at the tips of our own DNA.

As Dr. West recounts in his book, *The Immortal Cell*, the name of the company came to him while working late one evening in his lab at Baylor University, a private Christian instititution in Waco, Texas. Dr. West grew up in an Evangelical household, and as part of his religious studies, he had read the New Testament in Greek. That night, he recalled a passage from the Gospel of John. In the passage, Nicodemus asks Jesus, "How can a man be born when he is [*geron*] old? Surely he cannot enter a second time into his mother's wound and be born again?"

The New Testament uses the Greek word *geron*, which means "old man." *Geron* also serves as the root of the word for the scientific study of aging—gerontology. Thus, Dr. West's company would be named Geron.

While biblically inspired, it would take something other than divine intervention to get Geron off the ground. It would take cash, and a lot of it. Dr. West soon learned that asking investors to throw thousands or millions behind a student with no significant business experience to start a company in a field that had a reputation for attracting snake oil salesmen was a tough sell. The rejections piled up as Dr. West's savings dried up. But then came a glimmer of green-laden hope. Dr. West learned of an elderly, wealthy man living in a seaside Santa Barbara community who was distressed by his own impending mortality and had a history of funding projects he hoped could give him a few more years.

Dr. West set up a meeting and flew from Texas to the potential investor's offices in California, confident he would convince the old man that Geron could produce the life-extending science he had been searching for. Dr. West entered the man's office, set up his carefully crafted slides, and began his pitch. Not more than ten minutes into the presentation, his audience of one had been reduced to zero. The financier of his future was still alive, but stone-cold asleep. Feeling defeated, Dr. West made his way back to Texas, leaving much of his optimism behind him.

As he recounts in *The Immortal Cell*, the seemingly sound and practical advice given by those around him began to sink in. Perhaps it was best to finish his MD, then seek grant funding to start a lab focused on the telomerase question. It would be a lonelier, slower route—but most likely his only option.

Then, in what Dr. West describes as the "eleventh hour," hope once again came ringing on the telephone. This time, it was one of Dr. West's former fellow students, Karl Riabowol. Riabowol had a friend, Bill Ryan, an MD, who worked as a biotech analyst at what was then Citigroup's wealth management branch, Smith Barney. Believing the Wall Street firm may have an interest in Geron, Riabowol contacted Ryan and managed to get Dr. West a meeting.

With an empty checking account and piles of neglected schoolwork, Dr. West traveled to Smith Barney's Midtown, New York City conference room for one last rodeo. He dove into his usual, but sincere spiel, explaining the opportunities that lay ahead if the worlds of gerontology and biotech collided. This time, the pitch worked.

A short few weeks after the Midtown meeting, Geron cashed its first investor's check. Receiving funding from an MD and biotech analyst added significant weight to Geron's credibility as a company, and more checks began to arrive. The bank account for his fledgling company accumulated $250,000 in assets. It was enough to rent an office in a building across the street from Baylor's medical school, but not enough to disrupt the world of gerontology and biotech.

Before long, playing the triple-role of student, CEO, and lab scientist began to take its toll on Dr. West's sleep cycle. He was beginning to doze off one afternoon while wearing his student-hat when once again the phone rang. This time a representative for Alan Walton—a well-known and deep-pocketed venture capitalist—was calling. Walton had circumnavigated the globe looking to invest in a biotech company focused on aging, and three different sources had led him to Geron. Dr. West was now wide awake.

The phone conversation turned into another trip to New York City, which in turn led to an invitation to the National Conference on Biotechnology Ventures in Redwood Shores, California. Walton introduced Dr. West on the mainstage before hundreds of hungry venture capitalists and people working in biotech, calling Geron Corporation "an up-and-coming leader in the field."

Dr. West launched into his presentation, giving it everything he had. Passionate about the cause, but also aware of his audience, he explained science was at the brink of finding the gene that controls aging and that once located, a new era of medicine would be unleashed. This would open investors to a multi-trillion-dollar market.

And his talk also opened him up to a multi-million-dollar opportunity. As Dr. West gathered his slides from the presentation and headed toward the door, he was abruptly stopped and surrounded by a group of conference attendees. They were all wearing matching badges that displayed the name: Kleiner, Perkins, Caufield, and Byers (KPCB). Anyone with or searching for money in the startup world would recognize the KPCB acronym. It topped the Silicon Valley A-list of venture capital firms. KPCB had Amazon.com, AOL.com, Genentech, and a laundry list of other mega-companies behind its name—and now it was interested in Geron.

In a side room connected to the auditorium, Dr. West shook hands with the KPCB representatives, committing to allow them to lead Geron's financing. A few months later, he loaded his U-Haul and made the trip from Dallas to the San Francisco Bay area. Now, the race to find the human telomerase gene was on. Dr. West assembled an all-star team, including Dr. Hayflick, Dr. Blackburn, Dr. Greider, and Dr. Gregg Morin. They, and others, served as collaborators, advisers, or Geron employees all dedicated to the same end goal of locating the six-letter sequence that would decode human telomerase.

It was now approaching the mid to late 1990s, and years of work had still not yielded the results Dr. West wanted and Geron's board demanded. Despite his impressive team and countless rigorous lab tests, the gene sequence was still hiding somewhere in the abyss of our DNA. With today's technology, finding a gene can take a matter of minutes. In the 1990s, locating and isolating a gene was more difficult than finding a needle in a haystack. The task was not insurmountable, but it was an Everest of a mountain to climb.

Regardless of its difficulty, Geron was a publicly traded company and its survival depended on Dr. West's ability to find the "immortality gene" in human cells. Investors were becoming impatient, and Geron was beginning to lose its credibility as an aging-focused company.

Dr. West bet his resources and his team's time on the belief that human telomerase would have a similar DNA sequence as Dr. Greider's pond-dwelling *Tetrahymena*. Although little resemblance exists between the simple freshwater organism and human beings, Dr. West thought genes with such fundamental roles as telomerase remained mostly constant—even after evolutionary splits that occurred billions of years in the past.

The search to locate telomerase had been a marathon, but it became an all-out sprint overnight when the Geron team learned that a leading figure in cancer research, Dr. Robert Weinberg of Massachusetts Institute of Technology (MIT), may have found the human telomerase gene. Geron had risked the credibility of the company on being the first to locate the gene, and now there was a real threat of someone else publishing the gene's sequence before them.

In the little time red-eyed Geron employees slept after learning the news of Dr. Weinberg's research, it was on cots set up in the lab. They thought they may already be too late, and the stakes were too high to waste a moment of time. If they failed, so did the company. For two weeks, they lived this way until they found what they had been looking for: TTAGGG.

With these six letters identifying the human telomerase gene, they rushed to send their results to the journal *Science*. Their paper would be published in the August 15, 1997 edition. Dr. West and his team waited anxiously, knowing Dr. Weinberg's results could be released earlier in a competing journal. Finally, on that day in the middle of August, Dr. West's paper, which he gave the less-than-layperson-friendly title "Telomerase Catalytic Subunit Homologs from Fission Yeast and Human," hit the shelves. Exactly one week later, Dr. Weinberg's paper was published in the journal *Cell*.

At a party celebrating Geron's success, a banner hung that read "We won our Telome*race*."[64]

CLINICAL DEVELOPMENT FOR
TELOMERE EXTENSION TREATMENTS

The first time telomerase was used on human cells was with skin cells plucked from Dr. Hayflick himself. Dr. West thought he would use the biologist's cells to find the *true* Hayflick limit.

The legendary scientist was one of the many critics at the time who believed the process of human aging was too complicated to be manipulated by an intervention as seemingly simple as activating telomere growth through telomerase.

---

64   Michael West, *The Immortal Cell* (New York: Doubleday, 2003), 90–125.

Dr. West brought the results of the study to Dr. Hayflick's home overlooking the Pacific Ocean in Sea Ranch, California. Over dinner, Dr. West told him what he had found in the petri dish. When given telomerase, there was no Hayflick limit—Dr. Hayflick's cells had become immortal.[65]

While the ability of telomerase to lengthen telomeres in human cells is now widely accepted in the scientific community, more than twenty years later there is still no FDA-approved telomerase therapy.

But that could change in the near future. Dr. West is one of the scientists who believes they are close to developing a therapy ready for clinical development. AgeX Therapeutics—a company Dr. West founded since leaving Geron in 1998—is currently testing an experimental treatment that combines telomerase gene therapy and induced tissue regeneration (iTR) technology. At the time of this writing, it is being assessed in animal studies with the hope of moving toward human trials in coming years to reverse developmental and cellular aging in humans, targeting age-related degenerative conditions.

Along with proving effective in elongating telomeres and stimulating rejuvenation in human cells, experimental treatments using telomerase will also have to quell fears that lengthening telomeres will not lead to the development of cancer. As shown in the infamous HeLa cells taken from cancer patient Henrietta Lacks in 1951, cancer cells continue to proliferate and metastasize due to an overactive expression

---

65 West, 90-100.

of telomerase. The correlation between cancer cells and telomerase is the leading argument among critics warning against the development of a telomerase treatment.[66]

Still, two decades after the Geron's team discovered a gene that effectively immortalizes cells, why don't we yet have a treatment that rejuvenates our aging cells as they approach the Hayflick limit and senescence?

For one, says Dr. West, progress in science can take time. When Geron first located human telomerase in 1997, it had been after six years and 40 million dollars' worth of research. Now, with innovations in machine learning, genes can be located in a matter of minutes for a tiny fraction of the cost.

But the passing of time alone will not cure the health consequences of aging. Scientists need funds to support the research that leads to their discoveries. Although uncovering the mechanisms of aging could lead to cures for the leading and most expensive chronic diseases, researchers devoted to studying the biology of aging are only allotted roughly 3 percent of the NIA's total budget, as mentioned previously.

This is not a new problem. Dr. West recalls watching the release of grants announced by the NIA when he was a graduate student in the 1990s.

---

66   Mohammad A. Jafri, "Roles of Telomeres and Telomerase in Cancer, and Advances in Telomerase-Targeted Therapies," *Genome Medicine* 8, no. 1 (2016): 69.

One $200,000 grant was dedicated to examining the most effective sole thickness in shoes to increase balance for the elderly. Another one, he remembers, measured the effect of the color on walls in nursing homes on residents' moods.

"This is where the money has been spent and continues to be spent," says Dr. West.

If we reverse aging, reasons Dr. West, the elderly can be outside playing with their grandchildren in the sunshine instead of looking at a wall—albeit a colorful one—in a nursing home.

Reversing aging should be science's primary aim, for it is the noblest of all human goals, he says. The objective, Dr. West emphasizes, is not to extend the time someone spends in a decrepit state in a nursing home but to give people more healthy, meaningful, and energetic years on the planet.

He wishes this science had arrived in time to save his father, Fred West. The elder West owned a truck business and had earned the reputation of being a "fixer," whether it was mending the city's snowplow in the middle of the night or replacing a missing part on a truck. But when he had a heart attack, no one knew how to fix him.

"The reason some of us work on this sort of thing is we want to put an end to that kind of loss," says Dr. West. "The world is a poorer place without my father in it, and when you multiply that by the millions and millions of people who suffer losses like that every day, this is a wonderful thing for scientists to work on, and it's certainly my motivation personally."

CHAPTER 6

CELLULAR SENESCENCE

Senescent cells are dormant, zombie cells that do not divide or support the tissues in which they are located. If not cleared away, senescent cells emit harmful toxins that accelerate aging and cause other cells to become senescent. The number of senescent cells increases over time as we age.

As the young cell biologist Dr. Leonard Hayflick taught us in his then-provocative theory on aging, normal human cells go through roughly fifty to seventy cell divisions before the protective caps on our chromosomes—telomeres—shorten to a critical limit and can no longer preserve the genetic information stored in our DNA. Our cells then stop dividing altogether—they reach the Hayflick limit. Dr. Hayflick called this inactive stage cellular senescence.[67]

When cell meiosis comes to a halt and a cell becomes senescent, it is programmed to self-destruct. This process is called apoptosis. However, on occasion, the programmed

---

67   Leonard Hayflick, "The Serial Cultivation of Human Diploid Cell Strains," *Experimental Cell Research* 25, no. 3 (1961): 585-621.

cell suicide fails and the cell is left in limbo. Luckily, our body has a backup mechanism to take out the trash. Senescent cells that do not commit apoptosis emit inflammation, creating toxins to alert our immune system that they need to be cleared out. But as we grow older, our immune system weakens and our internal janitors can no longer perform their job like they once did. Thus, the number of senescent cells begins to accumulate, and that is when the trouble starts.

These dormant inflammation-causing cells are often referred to as zombie cells. Like the disagreeable creatures in *The Walking Dead* and other zombie apocalypse productions, these cells are neither alive nor dead, but they can wreak havoc on your body and turn other living, healthy cells into zombies like themselves. Instead of spreading their infection through a fatal bite, senescent cells corrupt healthy cells by emitting toxic chemicals and damaging their DNA. The result? Accelerated signs of aging, such as grey hair, wrinkled skin, and an increased likelihood of age-related diseases, including cancer.[68]

Fortunately, researchers and entrepreneurs are working on technologies to save our bodies from the cellular zombie apocalypse that threatens our health as we age.

Gary Hudson is one of them. Hudson did not grow up watching zombie thrillers. He was more interested in the idea of humans living outside of the Earth's atmosphere and in neighboring solar systems. As a boy coming of age in the 1950s and 1960s, he witnessed man's first encounter

---

68 López-Otín, 1194-1217.

with the black vastness of space and watched the Apollo 11 moon landing in 1969. The deluge of space-themed science fiction novels inspired by these pivotal moments in history captivated his young mind and stretched the limits of what seemed possible for mankind to achieve—including how long we could expect to live.

"Long lives were a trope of many of those stories," Hudson recounts. In one such series of short stories by writer James Blish, the novels are marked by two notable scientific discoveries: the anti-gravity device—the "Dillon-Wagoner gravitron polarity generator"—which allows entire cities to roam the galaxy, and anti-death drugs, which Blish referred to as anti-agathics. Together, these two technologies gave humans the new promise of eternal life and the ability to explore uncharted territories of the galaxy.

The possibilities in space exploration and aging consumed Hudson's imagination as a boy, and later influenced his career path. But he could not choose both. He was initially inclined to choose aging but was ultimately persuaded to go in a different direction.

"I began my career intending to work on aging first. But I was dissuaded from this course of action by my advisor, who told me that the field was immature and also disreputable," he recalls. The thought was that "only cranks or Nobel laureates could spend time thinking about aging (the latter being pretty much immune to criticism and the former inured to it)."

It was not bad advice. As a college dropout with no degree to his name, Hudson employed his unbounded vision of what could be to win over the imagination of wealthy investors and convince them to join him in building the commercial space industry. Over the past half-century, Hudson helped launch and grow several private spaceflight companies. Most notably, he founded the Rotary Rocket Company, which built a landing test simulator for a reusable rocket that flew three successful flights in the late 1990s.

Although it had remained on the sidelines, his childhood fascination with aging stayed with him through adulthood. And when he turned fifty, he decided to once again make aging his focus.

In the early 2000s, Hudson heard a speech given by the bio-medical gerontologist and longevity evangelist, Aubrey de Grey, PhD. Much like himself, Dr. de Grey pushed people to think beyond where their mind and dreams had dared venture. He believed the process of aging, and the suffering that accompanied it, was not immutable. Aging, argued Dr. de Grey, could eventually be controlled, or even reversed.

Hudson resolved to help Dr. de Grey spread the word that the time to take command of the hands on our biological clock was now.

Using almost a quarter of his net worth at the time, Hudson donated to the longevity advocacy non-profit, the Methuse-lah Foundation, and eventually helped fund Dr. de Grey's aging research organization, the Strategies for Engineered Negligible Senescence (SENS) Foundation and much of his early work—including conferences he held in the United Kingdom at the University of Cambridge's Queens College.

Hudson was eager to get the top scientific minds on board. He said his goal "was to not-so-gently beat up my academic friends in the gerontology field who were scared to death to talk about any translational progress in aging, fearing for their reputations and grant funds."

He was frustrated by the lack of progress in the area, stating that "after more than thirty years, nothing had really changed from the time when my college advisors told me that the field was disreputable."

The reason why aging research deserves the minds of the best and the brightest scientists and the resources of the wealthy is simple, Hudson believes.

"No other field of biological science and medicine has the potential to alleviate suffering, add years of productive healthy life, and to delay the infirmities that come with aging than working on aging itself. Addressing only cancer, heart disease, etc. means you solve one problem. Working on aging means you solve many at one stroke."

At Dr. de Grey's first conference, Hudson heard a talk given by biochemist Judith Campisi, PhD, of the Buck Institute for Research on Aging. Dr. Campisi had done some pioneering work looking into the connection between senescent cells and aging, but research at that time was still more theory than fact.

Time passed, but Hudson continued to think about the role senescent cells played in aging. Over the coming decade, Hudson watched as research into senescent cells and their association with aging became more conclusive, and in 2014, he decided to enter the aging business himself.

Hudson teamed up with serial entrepreneur Matthew Scholz to found the senolytics company Oisín Biotechnologies. The term senolytics defines a class of treatments used to remove senescent cells. Oisín, based out of Seattle, Washington, faced the same technical hurdle as the other senolytics companies that had emerged as research on senescent cells advanced. How can you create a drug or technology that removes inflammation-causing senescent cells but leaves our healthy, properly functioning cells alone?

Oisín's approach to this problem was to create a patent-pending gene therapy technology that delivers a DNA program to all cells in the body. Once in a cell, the program interrogates the cell state—is it senescent or not (by asking if certain genes are turned on or off)? If the program determines the cell has gone senescent, then the program activates Caspase-9 (Casp-9)—a gene that induces cell suicide or apoptosis. Casp-9 is present in all of our cells, but is typically only activated in emergency situations—ridding the body of cells no longer performing their intended function and preventing them from going rogue. Activation of senescence during aging interferes with the apoptotic process in these defective cells, so the cells continue living, consuming energy, and causing harm in our bodies, even eventually inducing nearby cells to become cancerous. Oisín's approach provides the cell with a specialized version of Casp-9 that can only be activated by the Oisín DNA program, and only in senescent cells.

To avoid damage to healthy cells, Oisín's technology is programmed to read a cell's DNA and only kill that cell when it finds genetic markers of senescent or cancerous cells.

When Oisín's gene therapy was used in cell culture, they saw as much as an 80 percent reduction of senescent cells. The loss of senescent cells in mice was also significant. Outside studies have also shown a 25 percent increase in the lifespan of naturally aged mice when using senolytics, and a recently concluded Oisín study of aged mice showed similar benefits in the median survival of mice. Significantly, Oisín's mice only began to receive treatment at two years of age (the equivalent of a seventy-year-old human), and lived 20 percent longer than controls.[69] An even larger study, with five times as many animals, began in April 2020 and will conclude sometime in late 2021.

While Oisín plans to move to human trials as soon as 2020, assuming they receive regulatory approval and have sufficient resources, these trials—as with trials for other senolytics candidates—will not specifically target aging.

Since aging is not recognized by the FDA as a disease and is, thus, not a target endpoint for clinical trials, Oisín plans to avoid regulatory roadblocks by using the same strategy as other companies operating in the aging field and begin the trials by targeting a specific, recognized condition. For its first set of trials, Oisín will focus on using its technology to attack cancerous cells in a variety of tumors. Pending

69 "Great Results," *Oisín Biotechnologies*, June 3, 2020.

approval from the FDA, phase 2 of the trials would continue with the best responding variety of tumor.

One senolytics company, Unity Biotechnology, has already entered phase 2 of clinical trials. Unity is aiming to treat osteoarthritis with its drug candidate, UBX0101. A 2018 human phase 1 study showed that the senolytic reduced pain and improved function in patients suffering from osteoarthritis of the knee.[70]

Unity has piqued the interest of some of America's investment titans, including Jeff Bezos, Peter Thiel, and Fidelity Investments.[71] Unity went public in May 2018 and, at the time of this writing, has a market value of just under $400 million.[72]

Although investments in Unity demonstrate the growing interest in America's already multi-trillion-dollar longevity sector, encouraging developments have not convinced enough investors to lay down the money necessary to fully support researchers and entrepreneurs working in the field. For venture capitalists who want a quick and reasonably reliable return on their investment, aging-related biotech is an exceedingly risky investment that, even if successful, might not be profitable for multiple years or a decade.

---

70 "Unity Biotechnology, Inc. Announces First Patient Dosed in Phase 2 Study of ubx0101 in Osteoarthritis of the Knee," *Unity Biotechnology*, 2019.

71 Matthew Herper, "A Biotech Entrepreneur Aims to Help Us Stay Young While Growing Old," *Forbes*, 2018.

72 "Unity Biotechnology, Inc. Common Stock." Nasdaq. Accessed July 5, 2020.

But usual formulas, risk assessments, and short-term versus long-term profit calculations should not be applied in the same way as when a firm or wealthy individual considers investing in an app or latest hot new idea coming out of Silicon Valley, Hudson believes.

For those who have the resources, the number they should be concerned about is not a numeric value that follows the dollar sign, but the number of healthy years they have left on Earth to spend with those they love.

"The message I like to give people who have the resources to financially support work in aging in general, and Oisín in particular, is simple: do you want to be the richest person in the graveyard?"

"For the first time, science has given us the power to intervene directly in the aging process, and to ameliorate some of the worst consequences of growing old. It is always possible to make more money, but it is difficult to make more time. Oisín and related companies in the aging space have at least a chance to change this story of our lives."

CHAPTER 7

GENOMIC INSTABILITY

———

Genomic instability is characterized by damage inflicted on DNA through outside toxins, mistakes made during cell replication, and a breakdown of DNA repair mechanisms. Sufficient instability of the genome leads to accelerated aging and increases the likelihood of age-related diseases.

Dr. David Sinclair was four years old when he realized that he and everyone he loved would die. A grim revelation for a pre-kindergartner—although our inevitable mortality is a reality most children first come to recognize before their sixth birthday.

This unwelcome insight came from his grandmother, Vera. A tough Jewish woman who had fled during the 1956 Hungarian Uprising and immigrated to Australia, she was not one to coddle young minds by sugarcoating unpleasant truths through children's books. Instead, she let Dr. Sinclair know she and his parents would eventually leave him behind—and one day he would go too.[73]

---

73 Sinclair, *Lifespan: Why We Age—and Why We Don't Have To,* xi-xvi.

While the first acquaintance with death is profound, most children soon forget their impending mortality and return to more pressing matters, such as climbing trees and building sandcastles. Typically, this self-imposed amnesia lasts well into adulthood until we hit middle-age and realize we have likely hit or exceeded our lifespan's halfway point. Some scientists and psychologists believe this memory repression serves Darwinian purposes. How could we as a species concern ourselves with building shelters and gathering food if the thought of decomposing into the soil was constantly at the forefront of our minds?

But Dr. Sinclair did not forget, and he watched as his grandmother's bleak words materialized.

As he details in his book, *Lifespan,* his grandmother, growing up under Soviet oppression, spent her childhood and young adulthood knowing only violence and tyranny. But when she reached the shores of Australia, for the first time, she felt free. On occasion, she pushed the limits of what was even acceptable for women in liberalized countries such as Australia. In one such instance in the 1950s, Grandma Vera wandered onto Bondi Beach in a bikini, only to get herself kicked off for making a fashion statement that was too early for its time.

She continued to live this way, defying norms and expressing a childlike joy for life until her young spirit was overcome by her aging body. Dr. Sinclair's grandmother developed Alzheimer's, which slowly took her active mind and passion for life over the course of a long, painful decline.[74]

---

74 Ibid.

Although biology operates under the laws of nature rather than societal moral standards, Dr. Sinclair thought the elderly and their families deserved to be spared from the suffering that accompanies Alzheimer's and other chronic diseases.[75] And perhaps if he addressed the right questions in science, the laws of nature and aspirations of humanity could exist harmoniously together.

The questions that needed to be answered were: what is aging, can we control it, and if so, how?

Dr. Sinclair believes maintaining the stability of our genome is part of the answer.

Genomic stability is imperative to the health and survival of simple organisms such as yeast and much more complex organisms, including humans. Each coil of human DNA contains all of our genetic material. This information directs each function within our body. It is how our cells know how to keep our heart beating, legs walking, and lungs respiring. Put simply, without this information, we cannot walk, talk, or breathe.

Although our cells do what they can to protect the integrity of our genetic code, the system is not foolproof. Toxins including pollution, cigarette smoke, and other chemicals, can cause mutations within our DNA. Overexposure to the sun and viruses are among other sources of potential damage. Cells with damaged DNA still replicate, giving birth to new cells that also have a mutated set of genetic instructions. Although it does not happen often when we are young,

---

75   Ibid.

mutations within our DNA can even occur when healthy cells replicate. These new, genetically damaged cells do not have the set of instructions necessary to carry out their duties, making them dysfunctional and potentially cancerous.

In our youth, our body's repair mechanisms are like a well-oiled machine and manage to prevent most genetic errors from occurring. And although some mistakes still happen, they are few enough in number not to significantly impair our body's ability to operate. However, repair mechanisms break down with age and damage accumulates, eventually leading to a critical loss of information and the instability of our genome.[76]

So what can we do to prevent the breakdown in our repair mechanisms that accelerate as we age?

Dr. Sinclair and other researchers believe that part of the answer to that question involves restoring levels of a molecule associated with genomic stability—oxidized nicotinamide adenine dinucleotide, or NAD+—in our bodies as we age.

Some of his recent research has focused on one of the compounds that work to create NAD+ in the body, nicotinamide mononucleotide (NMN).

In the March 2017 edition of the journal *Science*, Dr. Sinclair and several coauthors published a paper outlining the results of NMN used in animal studies. He and his team at Harvard Medical School had put droplets of the molecule

---

76   López-Otín, 1194-1217.

in the water supply of elderly mice, hoping that increased NAD+ levels would enhance their cardiovascular strength. Then they waited and watched.

Within a week, the once old, frail, and weakened mice became stronger, faster, and leaner. When put on a mouse-sized treadmill, the NAD+ enhanced mice easily maintained the set pace while the untreated mice struggled to stay on the machine. The NAD+ mice clearly had the enviable endurance of a younger mouse.

With shinier coats, increased muscularity, and accelerated foot speed and strength, the physical improvements were obvious to even a layperson's eye. But the mice had also grown more youthful from within.[77]

As Dr. Sinclair told *TIME* magazine in March 2017, "We can't tell the difference between the tissues from an old mouse that is two years old versus a young mouse that is three to four months old."[78]

Chronologically, the elderly mice were still old, but biologically, they had gone back in time.

So what—on a molecular level—was NAD+ doing to create Benjamin Button-like mice?

---

77   Jun Li, "A Conserved NAD+Binding Pocket That Regulates Protein-Protein Interactions During Aging," *Science* 355, no. 6331 (2017): 1312-1317.
78   Alice Park, "Scientists Can Reverse DNA Aging in Mice," *TIME*, March 23, 2017.

Healthy people are born with sufficient levels of NAD+. It is critical to our brain function, energy levels, and, as Dr. Sinclair and others had surmised, the health of our DNA. However, as we grow older, our NAD+ levels begin to decline, diminishing our body's ability to protect the integrity of our genome. By the time we reach middle age, our NAD+ has declined by about half.[79] It appeared clear to Dr. Sinclair that this significant reduction in NAD+ was an important piece of the aging puzzle, and was worth pursuing further.

However, no clinical trial data currently shows NMN—the molecule that served as an NAD+ activator in Dr. Sinclair's mice study—can extend human life and healthspans. Dr. Sinclair's lab at Harvard is now hoping to prove through the clinical trial process that giving NMN to humans would have longevity-enhancing impacts comparable to the impact the increased levels of the molecule had in mice. At the time of this writing, NMN is currently undergoing human clinical trials at Brigham and Women's Hospital.[80]

NMN, however, is not the only NAD+ activating agent. While researching cancer biology at a Dartmouth University lab in 2004, Charles Brenner, PhD, discovered that nicotinamide riboside (NR) was a powerful vitamin precursor to NAD+.[81]

---

79 Michael B. Schultz, "Why NAD + Declines During Aging: It's Destroyed," *Cell Metabolism* 23, no. 6 (2016): 965-966.

80 "David Sinclair on NMN and Epigenetics," *Life Extension Advocacy Foundation*, September 10, 2019.

81 "Nicotinamide Riboside: From Discovery to Human Translation," *Charles Brenner Laboratory*, June 4, 2020.

Prior to uncovering the role NR plays in NAD+ creation, NR was a little-known and little-used molecule. Sixteen years later, Dr. Brenner's fortuitous discovery has remained a focus of his work and NR has become a key compound of interest in research regarding metabolism, cellular health, and aging.

However, although NR has created much excitement in aging research circles and his research has contributed to our understanding of the mechanisms of aging, Dr. Brenner bristles at the idea of being associated with "anti-aging."

Dr. Brenner warns that "the history of anti-aging claims is a morass of non-evidence-based salespersonship" and "simplistic notions."

"Some of the 'longevity' molecules marketed today are part of the same snake oil tradition as hundreds of other worthless elixirs," he says.

Dr. Brenner, now the director of the Obesity Initiative at the University of Iowa, exclusively studies conditions of metabolic stress in animals in which the NAD+ system comes under attack.

These conditions, says Dr. Brenner, "include obesity, alcoholic liver disease, heart failure, neurodegeneration, and coronavirus infection." He then looks for opportunities to do clinical trials to prevent or reverse these conditions in people when the NAD+ system is disturbed in the same way as it is in animals.

It is important to understand the many responsibilities the metabolism takes on in our bodies, and how metabolic health is critical to cellular repair and genomic stability.

Our metabolism is best known for breaking down nutrients from food and influencing the rate at which we burn calories, but it is also tasked with far more than determining the number we see on a scale.

"The metabolism is not only converting everything you eat into biological energy, but it is also converting what you eat into everything that you are and everything that you do," says Dr. Brenner. "Every single protein and lipid in your body, the structure of your cornea, your bones that are constantly undergoing renewal, the structure of your skin, the estrogen or testosterone you produce—everything in your body, unless you have an artificial hip, was made through your metabolism."

Quite literally, you are what you eat—through metabolic transformations.

The vital functions performed by our metabolism, including creating the energy necessary to carry out the cellular repairs required to maintain our genomic stability, can only be executed with the help of NAD+.

"You can describe NAD+ as the crown jewels of metabolism," says Dr. Brenner. "But unlike the crown jewels of England, which are inside of a safe inside of a vault, patrolled by guards inside of a castle, inside of another perimeter of guards, the crown jewels of metabolism are exposed to the elements."

"If we drink too much, if there is a viral infection, if we experience enough noise to induce hearing loss, if there is reactive oxygen damage, or if there is a sunburn," among a litany of other potential causes of cellular damage, including aging, this can cause a reduction in our NAD+ levels, and, thus, compromise our metabolism.

"I look at NR as a corrective measure," he concludes.

When our NAD+ system is attacked, increasing supplies of NR can ramp up NAD+ creation and bring our body back to homeostasis—the place it needs to be to function at an optimum level.

Unlike many of the compounds being investigated by aging researchers, NR is already available to the public in supplement form.

In 2012, the nutraceutical company ChromaDex licensed the vitamin derivative NR for both nutritional and therapeutic uses, but for the time being, has elected the over-the-counter route with its supplement product Tru Niagen.[82]

Choosing to develop a nutraceutical over a drug has both advantages and disadvantages.

As has been described previously throughout this book, pursuing FDA approval for a therapeutic drug often takes over a decade depending on the disease indication and costs an average of $19 million, with many longer-term studies of

---

82   "Tru Niagen," *Chromadex*, accessed June 4, 2020.

age-related conditions far exceeding the average.[83] This does not include the cost to actually develop a drug, which ranges from $2 to $3 billion, on average.[84] ChromaDex would also have to determine a different treatment indication for Tru Niagen, which is currently marketed as a product to aid in cellular health and healthy aging.[85]

But the supplement industry also has its limitations. While taking a longevity molecule from the lab to the supplement market can be done in a reasonable amount of time, nutraceuticals are not covered by insurance and products can be costly. Interested buyers must also scour through what can often be an endless assortment of options, many of which are low quality or fraudulent altogether.

But for those already suffering from age-related ailments, or for those hoping to take preventative measures to avert chronic illness in the first place, waiting up to a decade or more for a drug to gain FDA approval is not a workable option—especially when there is no guarantee their doctor will provide a prescription for a disease they do not have.

ChromaDex has taken steps to set its products apart from the snake-oil creams and fraudulent products that have plagued and created distrust in the aging and cellular health industry.

---

83   Thomas J. Moore, "Estimated Costs of Pivotal Trials for Novel Therapeutic Agents Approved by the US Food and Drug Administration, 2015-2016," *JAMA Internal Medicine* 178, no.11 (2016): 1451.

84   Joseph A. DiMasi, "Innovation in the Pharmaceutical Industry: New Estimates of R&D Costs," *Journal of Health Economics* 47, 20-33 (2016).

85   "Tru Niagen," *Chromadex*.

Tru Niagen has been reviewed by the FDA to ensure the safety of the product for human use, and NR is the subject of more than forty placebo-controlled trials "and may achieve health claims if such trials are positive," says Dr. Brenner. ChromaDex continues to partner with universities to further its research on NR and NAD+ and metabolic and cellular health.[86]

Dr. Brenner believes that positive results from previous NR trials should, of course, be followed-up with more narrowly tailored and long-term studies.

In an editorial in *American Journal of Clinical Nutrition,* he commented that based on small trials in which NR was shown to have anti-inflammatory activity or began to mobilize body fat in people, NR should be combined with exercise in longer trials in which people will be randomized based on fatty liver or body composition.[87]

"Such trials will not test longevity, but are designed to test improvements that are associated with better health," says Dr. Brenner.

The challenges, tribulations, and opportunities that come along with developing a drug or nutraceutical product are just some of the considerations entrepreneurs and scientists must examine when setting out with the focused intent of developing a treatment that will help people age better.

---

86   "Tru Niagen," *Chromadex.*

87   Charles Brenner, "Fat Mobilization without Weight Loss Is a Potentially Rapid Response to Nicotinamide Riboside in Obese People: It's Time to Test with Exercise," *The American Journal of Clinical Nutrition* (2020).

However, the promising science behind the connection between the stability of our genome and the quality of our health is clear, and making it easier for the public to access safe, effective, genome-stabilizing treatments is in everyone's best interest.

CHAPTER 8

MITOCHONDRIAL DYSFUNCTION

―――

Mitochondria are the "powerhouse" of the cell, creating the energy to carry out many cellular processes. However, as they age, their repair mechanisms breakdown and they emit harmful toxins that impact the health of other cells.

As a six-year-old first-grader, my pre-adolescent peers and I were like little energizer bunnies that had been charged with high-powered batteries. Often contributing to our teacher's heightened blood pressure, our small bodies appeared to actually be bottomless caverns of energy. To tame our excessive energy levels, we had two daily recesses where we climbed the monkey bars, ran up and down the soccer field, and scaled the purple toy—the largest structure on the Discovery Elementary playground. My teacher must have hoped that with a good forty-five minutes or so of athletic exertion, our class would remain in our chairs without jumping on top of them.

Nothing was particularly unique about the energy levels of the students in my first-grade class. Children of primary school age throughout the world experience the same soaring levels of energetic vigor that leave their teachers and parents feeling exhausted.

What makes the children of the world full of boundless energy? The answer, in part, is stockpiles of healthy, thriving mitochondria.

THE POWERHOUSE OF OUR CELLS

Mitochondria are frequently referred to as the "powerhouse of the cell." Situated in the cell's cytoplasm, the mitochondria are responsible for converting any food we consume into adenosine triphosphate (ATP)—the chemical that gives our cells the energy to carry out bodily processes, including building the muscle strength and supplying the energy that allows young six-year-olds to run across the playground.[88]

Although they are housed within our cells, mitochondria have their own genetic material—their own DNA. The story behind the mitochondria's genetic independence dates back over a billion years. It is believed that mitochondria were once their very own single-celled organism, much like bacteria, until they were swallowed up by larger cells, allowing for the eventual evolution of more complex organisms, including humans. When they formed a symbiotic relationship with

---

88 Lodish, H, A Berk, *Molecular Cell Biology*, 4th ed. (New York: W. H. Freeman, 2020).

larger cells all those years ago, they held on to their DNA
and have maintained it to this very day.

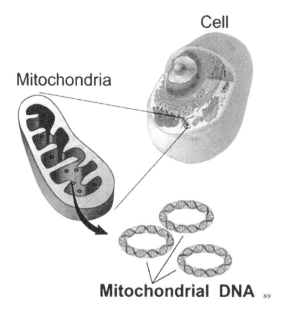

While the mitochondria's genome is much smaller and less
complex than it once was—and is peanuts in comparison
to the information stored in our cell's nucleus—it is still
critical to the mitochondria's ability to take on its important
task of turning nutrition into energy. Similar to the DNA
in our nucleus, the mitochondria's DNA is replicated when
mitochondria reproduce to create new mitochondria and
replenish the dysfunctional mitochondria that have been
recycled.[90]

89   "Mitochondrial DNA," *National Human Genome Institute.*

90   Michael W. Gray, *Genome Biology* 2, no 6 (2001): 1018.1.

When we are young and healthy, this process works like a highly functional Amazon packaging and shipping factory. The power of youthful mitochondria is evident in a child's ability to play endless games of chase without tiring, and in the college student who stays out all night dancing and can function—reasonably well—the next day. But as we age, the Amazon-like mitochondria factory begins to break down and function more like the Pony Express.

Scientists are working to determine why this decline begins to occur and accelerates as we age.

According to one theory about the role of mitochondria in aging, the very process used to create energy can become part of the problem. In one method the mitochondria use to create the power-giving chemical ATP—oxidative phosphorylation (OXPHOS)—free radicals are released as a toxic byproduct. These free radicals float around, damaging what lies in their path, including the mitochondria's membrane and its DNA.

The damage caused by the free radical byproduct can be both good and bad. First, the good. When harm to the membrane reaches a certain point, it sends out alert signals telling the body it is no longer healthy and needs to be removed and replaced by new, untainted mitochondria. Lysosomes, which serve as our body's waste-management system, heed the call from the impaired membrane and quickly work to break down the now old and inefficient mitochondria.

And now for the bad. Those free radicals can also cause significant damage to the mitochondria's fragile DNA. Along with other mutations, exposure to the toxins can disrupt the genetic code that directs mitochondria to use the OXPHOS process to create the ATP that feeds our body's energy needs. Now, instead of using the more preferred OXPHOS system of creating ATP, the mitochondria must use another less efficient process. This mechanism also does not produce free radicals as a byproduct, which means the mitochondria do not become damaged, and, thus, our lysosomes never come to the rescue when the mitochondria are old, dysfunctional, and in need of being recycled.

Intercellular happenings then get worse. With malfunctioning, non-OXPHOS mitochondria floating around in the cell's cytoplasm, unable to be broken down by lysosomes, the mutated DNA then gets passed on to new mitochondria when it's time to replicate. As the new generations of non-OXPHOS continue to proliferate, they eventually dominate the population of mitochondria within a cell. The proliferation of non-OXPHOS mitochondria also results in fewer NAD+ molecules in our cells. Since NAD+ is critical for many cellular processes, our bodies then attempt to create the molecule through a process other than OXPHOS. However, this results in the excretion of toxic free radicals called reactive oxygen species (ROS). ROS, through mechanisms still being investigated, then cause problems throughout our body, impacting other cellular processes and accelerating aging.[91]

While the molecular breakdowns that eventually lead to ineffective mitochondria appear to be quite complicated, it's exceedingly clear that these failures in the system increase as we age.

---

91 "How Age-Damaged Mitochondria Cause Your Cells to Age-Damage You," *Fighting Aging* (blog), 2006.

High-functioning mitochondria are evidently integral to maintaining a high-functioning body. For this reason, mitochondrial dysfunction has been identified as one of the hallmarks of aging.

TREATING MITOCHONDRIAL DYSFUNCTION

So what can be done to keep the engine running in our cell's powerhouse? Scientists are pursuing different strategies to tackle lapses in the mitochondria's repair mechanisms that become more apparent as we age. One method that may aid in the overall health of our mitochondria could be as simple as boosting our NAD+ levels through some form of supplementation with a product such as ChromaDex's True Niagen, as mentioned previously.

Another potential approach is the experimental drug J147. Researchers at the Salk Institute for Biological Studies originally investigated J147 as a possible drug candidate for Alzheimer's. Unlike many of the countless failed drugs attempting to treat the neurodegenerative disease, J147 did not specifically target amyloid plaques. Knowing that Alzheimer's is a disease of the aged brain, Dave Schubert, PhD, Salk professor and head of Salk's Cellular Neurobiology Laboratory, thought if they found a molecule that treats or reverses aging, instead of taking the common amyloid plaque-fighting approach to treating the disease, it could also serve as a remedy for Alzheimer's.[92]

Since old age is the biggest risk factor for Alzheimer's disease, it is not an illogical approach. Once an individual is above the

---

92 "Salk Scientists Develop Drug That Slows Alzheimer's in Mice," *Salk Institute for Biological Studies*, 2013.

age of sixty-five, a person's risk of developing the disease doubles about every five years. Despite this undisputed link and countless failed clinical trials, focusing on aging as a drug target for treating Alzheimer's has been largely overlooked.

"Alzheimer's disease research has traditionally focused on a single target, the amyloid pathway," Dr. Schubert said in a Salk news release, "but unfortunately drugs that have been developed through this pathway have not been successful in clinical trials. Our approach is based on the pathologies associated with old age—the greatest risk factor for Alzheimer's and other neurodegenerative diseases—rather than only the specificities of the disease."[93]

"We know that age is the single greatest contributing factor to Alzheimer's, so it is not surprising that we found a drug target that's also been implicated in aging," said Salk researcher Joshua Goldberg, PhD.[94]

So far, the evidence says the Salk team is right. In May 2013, scientists at the Salk Institute published a paper in the journal *Alzheimer's Research and Therapy*, demonstrating the memory-enhancing and youth-giving results when J147 was given to twenty-month old mice genetically engineered to show advance symptoms of Alzheimer's. These results came after three months of treatment.[95]

---

93 Ibid.
94 Ibid.
95 Marguerite Prior, et al., "The Neurotrophic Compound J147 Reverses Cognitive Impairment in Aged Alzheimer's Disease Mice," *Alzheimer's Research & Therapy* 5, no. 3 (2013): 25.

"I was very surprised when we started doing experiments with how big of an effect we saw," Dr. Schubert said about the studies. "We can give this to old mice and it really elicits profound changes to make these mice look younger at a cellular and molecular level."[96]

In another study attempting to compare the effectiveness of J147 when tested against the commonly prescribed Alzheimer's drug Aricept, J147 proved to be as effective, if not more so, according to the Salk researchers.

"In addition to yielding an exceptionally promising therapeutic, both the strategy of using mice with existing disease and the drug discovery process based upon aging are what make the study interesting and exciting," Dr. Schubert said back when the study was released. "[This is] because it more closely resembles what happens in humans, who have advanced pathology when diagnosis occurs and treatment begins."[97]

In a prime example of how key elements of potential medical remedies already exist in nature—and are perhaps in our kitchen pantry—Salk scientists developed J147 by creating a modified version of the molecule curcumin, which is found in turmeric. They have known for a while that J147 has regenerative properties, as the mice studies revealed, but they only discovered recently what the experimental drug was doing on a molecular level to enhance memory and restore youth. Turns out, it has to do with the mitochondria.

---

96 "Salk Scientists Develop Drug That Slows Alzheimer's in Mice," *Salk Institute for Biological Studies*, 2013.

97 Ibid.

In January 2018, Salk scientists published a paper in the journal *Aging Cell*, linking J147's regenerative factors to its ability to bind to the protein ATP synthase, which helps the energy-giving ATP inside the mitochondria. When bound to ATP synthase, J147 protected neurons from the toxins emitted by aged and mutated mitochondria. J147 also aided in the overall stability of the mitochondria and helped regulate mitochondria production.[98]

"This was the first demonstration that an Alzheimer's disease drug candidate targeting mitochondria can reduce the aging process of mitochondria at the molecular level," says Antonio Currais, PhD, the first named author on the paper. Since then, it has been shown that J147 increases the lifespan of model organisms such as flies and worms.

More recent studies on J147 and another drug candidate being studied by scientists at Salk—CMS121—offered additional evidence of the mitochondria's role in maintaining cognitive health and an individual's overall well-being.

"This study further validated these two compounds not only as Alzheimer's drug candidates, but also as potentially more widely useful for their anti-aging effects," says Pamela Maher, PhD, a senior staff scientist at Salk and coauthor of the new paper.[99]

98 Joshua Goldberg, et al., "The Mitochondrial ATP Synthase Is a Shared Drug Target for Aging and Dementia," *Aging Cell* 17, no. 2 (2018): e12715.

99 "Alzheimer's Drug Candidates Reverse Broader Aging, Study Shows," *Salk Institute for Biological Studies,* 2019.

"The bottom line was that these two compounds prevent molecular changes that are associated with aging," says Dr. Currais, who was also the first named author on the more recent manuscript.

J147 passed the FDA's toxicology test—meaning it proved safe when used in animals. With that hurdle cleared, it is now in phase 1 of clinical trials. During this stage, J147 will be given to a small group of human patients to ensure it is safe for human use. If J147 meets the necessary safety standards, it will then enter phase 2, where it will have to show that not only will it not cause harm, but that it is effective in treating its designated target condition—Alzheimer's.[100]

Although the links between mitochondrial health, Alzheimer's, and aging are becoming increasingly clear, even if J147 and CMS121 prove to be effective treatments for Alzheimer's and pass through the FDA with flying colors, healthy individuals looking to prevent the onset of age-related diseases may not have easy access to the drug due to aging not being recognized as a treatable condition by the FDA.

However, the Salk team is hopeful that if the TAME trial moves forward, J147 and CMS121 could potentially be used as drugs to treat aging.

---

100 "Salt Institute—J147," *Rejuvenation Roadmap*, accessed June 5, 2020.

CHAPTER 9

LOSS OF PROTEOSTASIS

———

Loss of proteostasis results from the breakdown of the body's protein building and repairing network, resulting in neuron-blocking and killing protein aggregates, among other life-threatening consequences.

On November 13, 1990, actor Michael J. Fox woke up in his hotel room to the bizarre sight of his pinkie finger on his left hand bouncing back and forth, seemingly by its own will. At the time, he was in North Central Florida filming the romantic comedy *Doc Hollywood* and figured the strange, independent movement was probably the consequence of downing a few too many beers with co-star Woody Harrelson the night before.

"Maybe we'd gotten into a slap-fight," Fox later wrote in his memoir *Lucky Man*. But the trembling did not stop, and in 1991, at the age of thirty, Fox received devastating news. The *Back to the Future* star had young-onset Parkinson's disease.

His doctor told him at the time that he had roughly ten good years left until the disease's symptoms would put an end to his acting career.[101] And that was the good news.

Fox managed to keep his disease hidden from the public for seven years, but in 1998, he came forward about his health in an interview with *People* magazine. Since his diagnosis, the tremors had progressed and the entire left side of his body suffered from stiffness. He could no longer keep it a secret. In the interview, he recalls one episode in January 1997 when he was sitting in a limo on his way to the Golden Globe Awards. The spasms in his left arm and leg were so dramatic he asked the driver to circle the block three times before finally dropping him off at the award show, where he would have to face the crowds and cameras.[102]

As Fox's diagnosis made clear, Parkinson's does not care who you are, what you do, or how much money you make. It is an indiscriminate, debilitating disease that will slowly strip your control over your own body. In 1999, before the Senate Appropriations Committee, Fox testified without the support of his medication. In what was at times an uncomfortable nine minutes to watch, the Hollywood star shifted back and forth in his chair, clasped his hands together to restrain his shaking arm from distracting the Senators from hearing his testimony, and struggled to turn pages as he pleaded the appropriators to increase funding for Parkinson's research.[103]

---

101 Diane Chun, "First Sign of Parkinson's Hit Fox During Filming," *The Gainesville Sun*, 2009.

102 Karen S. Schneider, "After the Tears," *People*, 1998.

103 "Michael J. Fox Testimony before the Senate," TV program, aired 1999, C-SPAN.

110 · FINDING THE FOUNTAIN

Over twenty years later, we still do not have a cure for Parkinson's, or the other most-feared disease of the brain, Alzheimer's. The lack of progress in the treatment of these diseases has cost families immensely, both emotionally and financially. It has also put a tremendous financial burden on our health care system.

NEURODEGENERATIVE DISEASES BY THE NUMBERS

Alzheimer's is America's most expensive disease. In 2020, Alzheimer's and other forms of dementia are expected to cost the country $305 billion, with Medicare and Medicaid paying for $206 billion of those costs. And with the expected increase in patients in years to come, total costs are predicted to spike to as much as $1.1 trillion by 2050.[104]

Caring for someone with Alzheimer's or dementia also places extensive and long-term emotional and financial stress on families. Caregivers provided approximately 18.6 billion hours of unpaid care. Over 40 percent of these caregivers come from households that earn less than $50,000 annually.[105]

This disease without a cure is also the most prevalent neurodegenerative pathology in the US and the sixth leading cause of death. At this moment, 5.8 million Americans are living and slowly succumbing to Alzheimer's. Without meaningful

104 "Primary Care Physicians on the Front Lines of Diagnosing and Providing Alzheimer's and Dementia Care: Half Say Medical Profession Not Prepared to Meet Expected Increase in Demands," *Alzheimer's Association*, 2020.

105 Ibid.

treatment, this number is expected to reach a harrowing 14 million by 2050.

Alzheimer's, similar to America's other top causes of mortality, becomes increasingly likely to develop with age. One in three seniors dies with Alzheimer's or other forms of dementia. The number of Alzheimer's-related deaths has skyrocketed as life expectancy in America and across the globe has risen. Between the years 2000 and 2017, deaths from Alzheimer's increased by 145 percent.[106]

Despite the disease's widespread impact, its very tangible health care price tag, and the over $30 billion that has been put into Alzheimer's research over the past several decades, little meaningful progress has been made. To date, the failure rate of an Alzheimer's drug moving through clinical trials is 99.6 percent.[107] And the failure rate of developing a drug that actually slows or reverses the development and spread of Alzheimer's is 100 percent.[108] Currently, only five approved drugs are available in the US for Alzheimer's treatment, and these only work to temporarily address some of the symptoms of the disease.[109]

These statistics and the forecasts of future trends—assuming we do not find a cure—are grim. The abysmal success rates

106 "Facts and Figures," *Alzheimer's Association*, 2020,
107 Cummings, Jeffrey L, "Alzheimer's Disease Drug-Development Pipeline: Few Candidates, Frequent Failures," *Alzheimer's Research & Therapy* 6, no. 4 (2020): 37.
108 Gina Kolata, "An Alzheimer's Treatment Fails: 'We Don't Have Anything Now," *The New York Times*, 2020.
109 "Treatment Horizon," *Alzheimer's Association*, June 4, 2020.

of drug candidates, and lack of any effective treatment, are in part due to the mysteries that still surround the disease.

We do know that neurodegenerative diseases such as Parkinson's and Alzheimer's seem to be, in part, a result of a loss of "proteostasis." The term is derived from two separate meanings—'proteo' for protein and 'stasis' for maintaining the current condition. Proteostasis is where our bodies want to be. When we are in this state, the network and processes that create our proteins are working properly without much error.

The breakdown of these systems leads to the loss of proteostasis—one of the hallmarks of aging. To understand the importance of maintaining proteostasis—and the consequences of its loss—it is necessary to first understand the role proteins play in our bodies.

THE MANY ROLES OF PROTEINS IN OUR BODY

Proteins are the workhorses of our bodies. They serve as antibodies, protecting us from foreign invaders such as bacteria and viruses. They function as enzymes, carrying out intracellular chemical reactions and helping with the formation of new molecules. Some proteins work as messengers, relaying information between cells, tissues, and organs so they can coordinate the activation of biological processes. Others provide structural support for our cells and help our bodies move, and some serve as a transport vehicle for small molecules that need to get from one place to another.

With such an extensive list of duties essential to a fully functioning body, a high-performing production system of the various proteins is critical. This system is referred to as the proteostasis network, which is also made up of proteins. The complex machinery that works together to create proteins is impressive in its execution; however, it is not flawless, and mistakes are made. With age, these mistakes grow more prevalent.

A misfolded protein is one such aberration that can result from a faulty protein-production cycle. When our protein-creating network is at its best, it can refold the proteins that have gone rogue or clear them from our bodies. But the system is not full-proof, and it decreases in efficacy in aging bodies.

A protein's shape is imperative to its ability to perform its designated function. It is akin to attempting to unlock a door with the wrong key. No matter how hard you try to cram a misfitted key into the keyhole, the door will remain closed. Thus, when something goes awry in a protein's construction, it can lead to what can become a big problem, including instructing the protein to perform the wrong task and the accumulation of protein aggregates.

Aggregates are clumps of misfolded proteins that have bound together. When these aggregations are not cleared away, they can form plaques. The accumulation of plaques formed by clumps of the protein beta-amyloid is a major indicator in the development of Alzheimer's, Parkinson's, and other neurodegenerative diseases.

The beta-amyloid plaques block and destroy neurons in our brains, preventing them from communicating with one another and transmitting the critical information necessary for our cells to carry out their designated jobs. In Alzheimer's patients, the neurons first impacted by these plaques are responsible for our memory. In more advanced cases, these plaques impair our neurons tasked with translating chemical signals related to our ability to reason, process language, and regulate our social behavior.[110]

Without the proper mechanisms to remove dysfunctional proteins, clear away plaques, or prevent aggregates from forming to begin with, misfolded proteins will continue to accumulate and spread over time—and we all know the end result.

By 2050, more than 250 million people alive today are predicted to develop Alzheimer's.[111] And another 12 million are projected to develop Parkinson's.[112] That means hundreds of millions of individuals will close the final chapter of their lives watching—hopelessly and helplessly—as their past and the people they love slip away from their memory. That is, if another age-related disease does not take them first.

NOVEL APPROACHES TO TREATING NEURODEGENERATION

Some companies are attempting to rewrite this preordained narrative by developing treatments that focus directly on

---

110 López-Otín, 1194-1217; "Loss of Proteostasis," *Life Extension Advocacy Foundation*, June 4, 2020.

111 "Facts and Figures," *Alzheimer's Association*, 2020.

112 Walter A. Rocca, "The Burden of Parkinson's Disease: A Worldwide Perspective," *The Lancet Neurology* 17, no. 11 (2018): 928-929.

attacking potential causes of the toxic protein aggregates that invariably appear in Alzheimer's and Parkinson's patients, and accumulate and spread as the diseases reach their more advanced stages.

One approach, currently spearheaded by Leucadia Therapeutics, is to restore the drainage mechanisms in the brain that typically work to remove toxic misfolded proteins in healthy individuals. This strays from the most common strategy used when attempting to treat neurodegenerative diseases—immunotherapy—a treatment that aims to activate the body's natural immune responses and its ability to fight pathologies.

Our bodies, much like the Drano you may use to clean a clogged shower, have an internal waste-management system. This is called the lymphatic system. In our central nervous system, it is called the glymphatic system. The pressure-washer that removes unwanted, toxic particles in our brains is called cerebrospinal fluid (CSF). CSF moves through the intercellular crevices of our brain, flushing out the garbage that impedes communication between our neurons and ultimately leads to their death. In young and healthy brains, the CSF flow is strong, and thus our memory retention and the ability to digest and process new information is typically at its best in our youth.

To picture what the breakdown of CSF flow looks like in our brains, "Think of a small creek in the forest," said Doug Ethell, PhD, founder and CEO of Leucadia, in an interview with Fight Aging!, an online outlet.

"Oak trees overhang the creek and occasionally a leaf falls in and gets carried away. In late summer, before the leaves change, the creek starts to dry up and leaves are carried away slower and slower, until a threshold is reached where they form a mat and then none of them are carried away," he explains. "The plaques in Alzheimer's disease are mats of amyloid-beta."

Dr. Ethell believes that by restoring the drainage system in the area of the brain where signs of neurodegeneration first begin to occur in Alzheimer's patients, it will slow or prevent the spread of toxic aggregates throughout the brain.

He says, "As it turns out, Alzheimer's disease pathology appears first in older parts of the cerebral cortex, called allocortex, where CSF is handled very differently than in the neocortex (the area of our brain that regulates our sense of hearing and smell). The allocortex is intimately connected to the olfactory system (the system that controls our sense of smell) and CSF that clears interstitial spaces in the allocortex drain from the brain to the nasal cavity through a porous bone called the cribriform plate."

He continues: "With age, apertures in the cribriform plate become occluded, and that can be accelerated by life events such as head injuries and broken noses. The net effect of those occlusions is an age-dependent slowing of CSF outflow, resulting in less efficient CSF-mediated clearance of the allocortex. Those leaves (the amyloid) start to accumulate and gum up the works, leading to an accumulation of factors that cause Alzheimer's disease pathology."

Leucadia believes a product they developed will help clear the mat of leaves from the congested river of the allocortex of a patient's brain, ultimately slowing the progression of Alzheimer's. The technology, named after the mythological Greek river nymph Arethusa, is surgically implanted at the top of the nasal cavity, where the cribriform plate is located. From that location, the device is designed to restore the flow of CSF in individuals suffering from mild cognitive impairment (MCI), with the hope of reversing their MCI and preventing the level of protein aggregates from reaching the critical point where MCI becomes Alzheimer's.

As of this writing, Leucadia plans to request approval from the FDA to pursue clinical trials to test its device in the near future. If proven successful, it would be the first treatment that actually halts or reverses signs of cognitive decline in Alzheimer's patients.[113]

As for Michael J. Fox, nearly thirty years after his fatal diagnosis, he is still standing—and fighting. He has become the face of Parkinson's advocacy but, still shy of his sixtieth birthday, he does not represent the average Parkinson's patient. As with Alzheimer's, the greatest risk factor for Parkinson's is age.

Fox has dedicated his life to curing the disease and his foundation alone, the Michael J. Fox Foundation, has raised over $900 million in research dollars. Its simple mission is to put themselves "out of business by finding the cure for Parkinson's."[114]

---

113 "An Interview with Doug Ethell of Leucadia Therapeutics," *Fighting Aging* (blog), September 10, 2017.

114 "The Michael J. Fox Foundation for Parkinson's Research," June 4, 2020.

But the United States' elderly population is growing, and the bulk of government and private research dollars continues to focus on the symptoms of the disease—not the underlying cause. Unless there is a fundamental shift in priorities, billions of dollars will continue to be spent and the Michael J. Fox Foundation will likely remain in business for the indefinite future.

CHAPTER 10

DEREGULATED NUTRIENT SENSING

———

The four nutrient-sensing pathways are IGF-1, mTOR, sirtuins, and AMPK. They are important regulators of metabolism and aging. Aging leads to disturbances in the normal functioning of these proteins, leading to the occurrence of age-related disease.

The children of Zeus and Themes included three goddesses—Lachesis, Atropos, and Clotho. These daughters were given the responsibility of weaving the threads of life and, therefore, the fate of humanity. They became known as "The Fates."

Each daughter was tasked with a different duty at the dawn of mankind. There was Lachesis the allotter, Atropos the inflexible, and Clotho the spinner. From their post on Mount Olympus, they wove the thread of each mortal's earthly existence from the time they were born until Atropos raised her scissors and cut the string, marking their death. Not even Zeus himself could override the way the Fates spun a mortal's wheel of fortune or destruction.

Clotho's power over the thread of life cemented her spot as a formative figure in ancient Greek mythology—and now her legacy has made its way into modern science.[115]

116

THE "LONGEVITY" GENE

It was 1997 and Dr. Makoto Kuro-o was leading a team using genetically engineered mice to study blood pressure. The investigation did not go as planned. Inexplicably, the mice began to age at an accelerated rate. Their skin wrinkled, their muscles weakened, and their health dramatically declined. The mice died after just two months,

---

115 "The Fates," *Greekmythology.com*. June 5, 2020.
116 Morphart Creation, *The three fates of Greek Mythology*, Image.

reducing their lifespan by 80 percent compared to the average mouse.[117]

Clearly, the scientists recognized, something in the lab had gone awry.

They paused the study and looked back, eager to uncover what could have caused such a dramatic acceleration in the mice's aging. They discovered that while engineering the mice for their research, they had accidentally disrupted a previously unknown gene in their DNA. Consequently, the expression of an unnamed protein encoded by this gene had become greatly depressed. The lack of this mysterious protein appeared to be the culprit behind the early death of the mice.

Dr. Kuro-o and his team wondered if the under-expression of this protein leads to accelerated development of chronic disease and a shorter life, would increasing its levels also extend the mice's number of healthy years?

Indeed, it did.

When the mice were engineered to express above-average levels of klotho, organ function strengthened, cognition sharpened, and the overall health of the mice improved. In fact, these mice lived 20 to 30 percent longer than the average mouse.

---

117 "Hormone Could Lead to a Fountain of Youth Research," *Los Angeles Times*, 2005.

Realizing the significance of their discovery and the regulatory power this new protein had over aging, it seemed fitting to call it "klotho."[118]

Jim Plante, CEO of Klotho Therapeutics, runs one of the biotech companies working to bring klotho-based treatments to the clinic.

As the mouse studies indicated, Plante believes that klotho is worthy of its namesake and has the potential to serve as a therapy for a host of chronic diseases and as a treatment to make us all more resilient to the passage of time.

"Aging is the risk factor for major chronic diseases, which are the leading cause of death," says Plante.

"That is the approach we should take to health," he elaborates. "Not just treating each of these diseases individually as its own stand-alone problem, but addressing what is common between all of these diseases—and that is aging."

An age-related disease eventually took his father.

As a young man, a few years after he graduated from college, his father became ill from a genetic disorder called Polycystic Kidney Disease (PKD). He was able to undergo a successful kidney transplant with the help of a family donor, but even with his new kidney, Plante's father passed away several years afterward from cancer.

---

118 Ibid.

Plante also learned that the genetic kidney disorder his father suffered from ran strong in the family bloodline, impacting most of his immediate relatives and himself.

"That is what got me interested in kidney disease in general," says Plante. "I recognized that kidney disease was a big underserved problem impacting many millions of Americans and people all over the world, and is a major burden on the health care system and costs."

According to the National Kidney Foundation, more than 37 million people in the US suffer from chronic kidney disease (CKD). Mature populations are at the greatest risk. One in every seven adults currently has CKD, and one in three American adults is at risk for developing the disease.

For the 80 million American adults at risk of eventually becoming a CKD patient, the diagnosis could be fatal. CKD is currently the ninth leading cause of death in the US. The rising number of Americans developing CKD is also a steep burden on government health programs. Annually, over $84 billion Medicare dollars were spent on treating CKD patients, and an additional $36 billion were spent on end-stage renal disease (ESRD) patients—individuals requiring dialysis or a kidney transplant.[119]

While Plante was determined to find an effective treatment for the diseases of the kidney likely to impact much of his family and countless Americans, he recognized that, as he

---

119 Centers for Disease Control and Prevention, "Chronic Kidney Disease Basics," accessed June 2, 2020.

saw with the death of his father, curing one chronic disease would only offer a temporary reprise until another debilitating disease surfaced in its place.

Plante thought, "How can we influence these chronic diseases of aging altogether?"

"That is how I got to klotho," he says.

In addition to its apparent universally positive impact on processes associated with aging, Plante was drawn to klotho because of its special relationship with the kidney. The kidney is the klotho protein's main site of production. Klotho expression has also been shown to be directly correlated with kidney health.

The levels of klotho in an individual's blood drop significantly in patients with CKD and continue to diminish as the severity of the disease increases. Inversely, there is evidence that treatment with the klotho protein improves kidney function and survival for individuals with CKD.

A 2017 mice study published in *Kidney International* showed that mice with CKD who were injected with the klotho protein experienced less kidney and heart damage than mice with CKD that were not treated.[120]

Since the serendipitous discovery of klotho in 1997, thousands of peer-reviewed studies have been published on the protein.

---

120 Ibid.

Klotho is produced in the kidney and the brain, then circulates throughout the body like a hormone. In general, just like any other human hormone, klotho levels can naturally be fairly diverse from one human to the next, but its expression is also impacted by a variety of outside factors, including age.

Klotho levels are the highest when you are a newborn but steadily dip lower as you grow and decline by about 50 percent by the time you reach middle-age. The drop continues—and at an accelerated pace—as you reach your later years and become plagued with a perpetual train of chronic disease.

The usual suspects of lifestyle behaviors can also impact the hormone's levels, including choices concerning nutrition, exercise, sleep, alcohol, and tobacco consumption.

In general, healthy choices result in higher levels of klotho, and unhealthy habits lead to depressed levels of klotho.

While klotho levels tend to fluctuate with age and lifestyle decisions in all humans, roughly 20 percent of individuals are born with a mutation in the klotho gene that leads to increased levels of expression of the klotho protein. Similar to the mice that scientists engineered to overexpress the protein, individuals with this mutation have been found to have an average IQ six points higher than those without the mutation, as well as have a longer lifespan with fewer chronic diseases.[121]

---

121 Dena B. Dubal, et al., "Life Extension Factor Klotho Enhances Cognition," *Cell Reports* 7, no. 4 (2014): 1065-1076.

How and why do klotho levels have such a significant impact on our lifespan, health, and brain cognition?

One important finding has been klotho's role as a regulator in the body's nutrient-sensing pathways.

Our bodies have sensors that determine how we process the nutrients we depend on to survive. They serve as key regulators in metabolic health and aging. Four main nutrient-sensing pathways are linked to longevity and the rate at which we age: mammalian target of rapamycin (mTOR), AMP kinase (AMPK), sirtuins, and insulin/insulin-like growth factor (IGF-1).

Ideally, these nutrient-sensing pathways can function so that our body uses nutrients efficiently and effectively. Doing so is critical so the body can perform routine processes, such as nutrient absorption and energy creation, as well as recovering from injury or warding off viral invaders.

However, as we age or are exposed to negative environmental factors that compromise the health of our cells, these pathways become defective and can no longer recognize or process nutrients at an optimal level. This deregulation of nutrient sensing leads to increased inflammation, inadequate use of nutrient sources, and accelerated aging. For this reason, deregulated nutrient-sensing has been characterized as one of the nine hallmarks of aging.[122]

But klotho may be able to serve as a therapeutic remedy to this breakdown. The neural-protective, anti-oxidative,

---

122 López-Otín, 1194-1217.

anti-inflammatory, and pro-survival properties of klotho work to block harmful age-promoting factors of some metabolic pathways when they become compromised, most notably IGF-1.[123]

Its role as a nutrient-sensing regulator is believed to be a leading factor in its regenerative properties, but questions remain about the full potential of the future of klotho-based therapeutics and how the protein operates at cellular and molecular levels in the body.

Dr. Dena Dubal is one of the scientists working to further explore some of the fundamentals of klotho's biology that remain a mystery.

Dr. Dubal is now an associate professor of neurology at the University of California San Francisco (UCSF), but she remembers what it felt like to first learn about the aging brain when she was sitting in a classroom as an undergraduate student at the University of California at Berkeley.

She was intrigued by the topics covered in her class about the physiology of aging, but her interest was piqued when they approached the section about the brain.

"When it came to the brain, I was at the edge of my seat," says Dr. Dubal. "I knew I wanted to learn and discover more in this area."

---

123 Xiangxiang Zhou, et al., "Klotho, an Anti-Aging Gene, Acts as a Tumor Suppressor and Inhibitor Of IGF-1R Signaling in Diffuse Large B Cell Lymphoma," *Journal Of Hematology & Oncology,* 10 no. 1 (2017).

As an undergraduate, Dr. Dubal also took a class in medical anthropology and became fascinated by how people in different cultures and socioeconomic groups throughout the world experienced disease.

Her dual interests of the physiology of the brain and anthropology led her to pursue a double major: anthropology and neurobiology.

"It was aging itself that bridged my interest in anthropology and how people experience their bodies and disease in light of culture and socioeconomic status with the actual physiology and biology of how we age," says Dr. Dubal.

She further recounts: "If in some way I could contribute to or affect the underlying process of aging itself—if one could help alleviate suffering from the diseases around aging, then that itself would be very impactful across cultures and socioeconomic statuses—it felt like a calling. I realized that what I wanted to do next was really dig into the biology."

Dr. Dubal now directs a lab in the Memory and Aging Center at UCSF's Weill Institute for Neurosciences, where she continues the digging she originally set out to do as an undergraduate.

She figures that if she can determine how to treat the aging process as a whole, the same mechanism could be applied as a treatment for individuals suffering from various forms of dementia, including Alzheimer's patients.

"Aging is the biggest risk factor for cognitive problems, and cognitive problems are one of the biggest biomedical challenges that we face," says Dr. Dubal. "Why don't we just block aging?"

Dr. Dubal believes—and her research attests—that klotho has the potential to at least delay aging and improve health.

In one study, she injected klotho into the stomach cavity of young and healthy mice, old mice, and mice suffering from a form of dementia similar to Alzheimer's.

"We found that those mice that had been treated had better brain function within four hours," Dr. Dubal says.

The aging brain is one of the conditions Plante's Klotho Therapeutics plans to treat, but acute kidney injury and CKD are the first disease indications the company will seek FDA approval for.

As with other companies in the aging space, although the treatment has the potential to benefit the longevity of all individuals, Klotho Therapeutics must choose a disease the FDA recognizes and has approved endpoints for.

"For something like acute kidney disease, it is very straightforward," says Plante.

However, in the future, the company could potentially use the framework of the TAME trial to test a klotho treatment aimed at delaying the onset of chronic diseases as a whole. This treatment could then be used by patients suffering from the consequences of aging or individuals simply interested in enhancing their longevity.

The ideal future scenario, says Plante, would be for an average person to have their klotho levels measured through a blood sample, and then therapeutically increase klotho in individuals with low baseline levels to move them into a healthy or more optimal range. This would be a similar approach to treating other hormones that tend to decrease with age, such as the thyroid hormone in women.

Klotho injections and small molecule pills that can increase klotho levels are among the potential methods of drug delivery.

But for now, this is an aspirational vision of the future. If clinical trials for a drug developed by Klotho Therapeutics is successful, only individuals suffering from the specific disease it received FDA approval for will benefit from the increased healthspan and neural-durability that klotho has shown to produce in animal studies—unless a doctor prescribes the medication off-label.

As both an MD and PhD, Dr. Dubal has seen the toll that bouncing from one chronic disease to the next takes on an individual's physical and mental health, and the emotional and financial strain it puts on families—as well as the government programs they depend on.

"We currently spend a third of our life with chronic diseases," she says.

"If we could make major headway in understanding the biology of aging itself, we could open powerful pathways to treatments for diseases that are expensive for the individual and to society."

Age-related deregulation of nutrient-sensing pathways deserves further exploration. We know the breakdown of these pathways leads to increases in inflammation, oxidative stress, cell death, and inadequate use of nutrients resulting in accelerated aging and disease.

We also know that klotho, a protein hormone, known for its ability to promote healthspan and longevity, has the potential to prevent the damaging effects of aging via its pro-survival, anti-oxidative, and anti-inflammatory properties.

The increasing aging population and the increasing number of elderly people with currently incurable chronic conditions—such as dementia, diabetes, cardiovascular, and kidney disease—have us facing unprecedented socio-economic and clinical challenges. Klotho-based therapeutics represent a promising avenue for the development of meaningful aging treatments.

CHAPTER 11

ALTERED INTERCELLULAR COMMUNICATION

———

Altered intercellular communication is the breakdown in communication via chemical signals between cells. The disrupted signaling influences aging and age-related diseases.

Nestled atop a rolling green hill in a mountainous region of northern Slovakia lies the ruins of Castle Čachtice. Today, the crumbling stone edifice is a relic of Europe's transitory period between the Middle Ages and the continent's early modern period. But, as legend has it, the walls of this ancient fortress hold more than just stories of battles between rival kingdoms. They are stained with the blood of some 650 young female victims.

Behind the corpses of the often preadolescent girls was one woman with a deadly desire to maintain her vitality and youth.

Countess Elizabeth Báthory was born a noblewoman in what was at the time the Kingdom of Hungary. According to folklore, as she grew older, the countess watched furiously as her smooth skin began to crack and nature seemed to steal the beauty she enjoyed in her youth. As someone who believed in the darker edges of the occult, she sought advice from trusted members of her court who practiced mysticism and witchcraft.

Countess Elizabeth Báthory

One proposed remedy to restore her youth was bathing in the blood of the young. Satisfied with the advice, the countess quickly assembled her team of sorcerers and alchemists and launched a campaign to lure the village's young girls to

---

124 *Blood Countess: Elizabeth Bathory, Anonymous Portrait, 17th Century,* History Today, Image.

the confines of her castle. As bait, she promised to cultivate these children of gentry into respectable women.

Bathing in blood was not the only incentive for the countess. It is said she also took pleasure in watching others suffer. Some versions of the story claim the countess subjected the girls to unthinkable methods of torture and murder, including one reputedly of her own invention—a femininely shaped, spiked coffin. She called it the Iron Maiden.

Unfortunately for Countess Báthory, even gallons of young blood taken from the hundreds of mutilated corpses stockpiled on castle grounds could not restore her youth. And eventually, villagers became suspicious of the whereabouts of its disappearing girls. Overwhelming evidence pointed to the countess's alleged elite young girls academy at Castle Čachtice. Her barbarism now exposed to the public, the countess was put on trial, found guilty, and spent the rest of her days locked in the confinements of a small tower in her castle of terror.[125]

Blood baths and bloody refreshments are some of the more morbid examples of humankind's quest to find the Fountain of Youth. But although Countess Báthory's approach was neither ethical nor effective, the supposed regenerative properties of young blood have withstood the ages and have continued to be a prominent theme in contemporary folklore.

---

125 "Death of Countess Elizabeth Bathory," *History Today*, 2014; John Malathronas, "'Blood Countess' in Slovakia: Tourists on the Trail of Elizabeth Bathory," *CNN*, 2014.

And now, purported regenerative properties in young blood have not only influenced studies in modern science but have also been exploited for commercial purposes.

Fortunately, some are challenging the centuries-old dogma surrounding the alleged power of young blood. Bioengineers Irina Conboy, PhD, and Michael Conboy, PhD, maintain that focusing on the pro-youth qualities of young blood misses the point. Science must instead turn its attention to the pro-aging factors in old blood.

DEBUNKING YOUNG BLOOD MYTHS

Dr. Irina Conboy and Dr. Michael Conboy share a lab at The University of California at Berkeley. Here, the married couple has established themselves as leading thinkers in the field of aging research, and have published pioneering work concerning the impact of aged blood on stem cell behavior.[126]

Similar to many of her peers working in aging research, Dr. Irina Conboy had an early fascination with aging.

"When I was five or six," says Dr. Irina, "I noticed that I was getting physically bigger."

Observing this, Dr. Irina tried to project how her body would continue to develop. "When you cannot fit under the table anymore, what happens next?" she remembers contemplating as a young girl.

---

126 "The Conboy Laboratory," *Berkeley Engineering*, accessed April 5, 2020.

Forecasting even further into the future, she realized that one day she would become old and, eventually, her skin would wrinkle like her grandmother's. She saw that beyond the physical appearance of her withered skin, her grandmother's overall well-being suffered because of her advanced age. "I felt pity and I wanted to help her live longer," she says.

But despite her early interest in aging, her journey to becoming a recognized aging scientist is far from a likely one.

Irina was born in Moscow when it was still the command post of the Soviet Union. Adding to the challenges of growing up in a communist regime, she was Jewish at a time when the government and culture were still rampant with anti-Semitism. In what seemed like a lucky break, Irina was recruited at the age of six to begin training as a gymnast. As a potential future Olympic athlete wearing the Soviet flag, she was rewarded with better food and new clothes. But several years later, she broke both arms while training, ending her career as a gymnast and any potential future spot on an Olympic podium. Without the full strength of her limbs, she would now need to rely on her brain to have a successful professional career. Her new academic focus brought her back to her childhood curiosity about aging.

Irina's life took another turn when Mikhail Gorbachev, the Soviet Union's eighth and final leader, came to power. Under his leadership, tensions between the Western and Eastern bloc began to ease and the young academic had the freedom to visit a childhood friend who was studying at Harvard University. To free herself of host duties and carve out some time for studying, Irina's friend had lined up a series of dates for her visitor with colleagues from the Harvard lab where she worked. Dates were scheduled throughout the week.

Michael Conboy was "Thursday." A date to the disco turned into several years of a long-distance relationship and, eventually, "Thursday" became Irina's husband. After marrying, the couple both pursued PhDs at Stanford University's Department of Biological Sciences. Here, they began to focus their work on answering the question so many had pondered before them: Could blood from the young be used to rejuvenate the old?[127]

For her postdoctoral work in Dr. Thomas Rando's lab at Stanford, Dr. Irina was particularly interested in studying how muscle repair changes over time. Why do our stem cells readily repair and build our muscles after a rigorous session in the gym when we are young, but as we grow older, this system begins to break down and, eventually, we are just left with tired, sore muscles?

Dr. Irina Conboy hypothesized that deterioration of muscles and vital organs over time was due to a breakdown in intercellular communication—which has now been identified as one of the hallmarks of aging.

It is believed that the breakdown in intercellular communication as we age is in large part a consequence of several of

___

127 The Florida Institute for Human & Machine Cognition, "Episode 91: Irina and Michael Conboy Explain Tissue Repair and Stem-Cell Rejuvenation," accessed June 27, 2020. In *STEM—Talk*, Podcast.

the other hallmarks of aging, including the inflammation created by over-accumulation of harmful senescent cells. This build-up of a toxic environment interferes with the cellular chemical interchanges required to ensure our immune system, tissue repair, and all other bodily processes function at full strength.

In the early 2000s when the Conboys were postdoctoral students, research had already shown certain signaling pathways between cells directed stem cells to begin the process of building organs when we are just embryos. Dr. Irina wondered if the same communication pathways were responsible for muscle and organ repair throughout our lives, and if they were being inhibited as we grew older.

To test this theory, she used a technique called parabiosis. The term means "living beside"—and that is exactly what it looks like in practice. It is used to study the impact on organisms when two partners are surgically conjoined, linking their internal organ and circulatory systems. For their research, the Conboys used a technique called heterochronic parabiosis—the surgical joining of a young and old partner. In what to an untrained eye may look like a scene from Frankenstein's lab, a young healthy mouse and an elderly mouse with all the defects of old age were sewed together to become one. When completed, the parabionts looked like Siamese twins that have somehow been born decades apart.

Heterochronic Parabiosis
by Mckenzie Deutsch

But within a short period, the age gap between the parabionts appeared to shrink. The muscle tissue in the older mouse strengthened, its liver was regenerated to a healthier state, and its cognitive capabilities sharpened. However, the parabiont relationship was a zero-sum partnership. The younger parabiont did not maintain all the benefits of its youth. It effectively gave its youth away. While the older mouse became stronger and healthier, the younger mouse became weaker, developing chronic inflammation, a compromised immune system, and deteriorating organs.

They published their findings on parabiosis often in collaboration with or alongside other researchers trying to answer questions surrounding the qualities of young and old blood, including Stanford University's doctors Thomas Rando, Irving Weissman, and Tony Wyss-Corey and Amy Wagers, who is now at Harvard University.[128]

From the outset, the Conboys were hesitant to put too much weight on the potential power of young blood. They surmised that the results of the experiment may have been influenced by the younger mouse's healthier organs and immune system, putting into question whether the potential regenerative impact of young blood may not deserve all the credit. To clarify these results, they performed heterochronic blood sharing, which only allowed for the exchange of blood.

Within five days, the results of the study began to reveal themselves. The older mouse again showed improved muscle tissue, organ function, and neural acuteness. But the most dramatic findings were the negative effects on the younger mouse.

"Investigating muscle, liver and brain hippocampus, in the presence or absence of muscle injury, we find that, in many cases, the inhibitory effects of old blood are more pronounced than the benefits of young, and that peripheral tissue injury

---

128 "Irina M. Conboy's Research While Affiliated with University of California, Berkeley and Other Places," *Researchgate*; "Michael Conboy," *Researchgate*; "Irving L. Weissman," *Researchgate*; "Tony Wyss-Coray," *Researchgate*; "Amy Wagers, PhD," *Harvard Stem Cell Institute*; "Selected Publications," *Rando Laboratory*.

compounds the negative effects," they wrote in a 2016 article in *Nature Communications*.[129]

The Conboys determined that unlike much of the prevailing science and mythology, perhaps we should not be paying attention to the properties of young blood but the negative elements of old blood and the harmful environment they create for stem cells tasked with rebuilding our tissues. In other words, while young blood did have regenerative factors, the "pro-aging" factors in old blood were stronger, and if they were to compete against each other in a 50/50 exchange, the old blood would dominate every time.

Upon examining the blood plasma, they found a higher prevalence of certain proteins in old blood blocked the intercellular communications notifying stem cells that tissue repair was needed. Stem cells living in tissues surrounded by younger blood did not have this problem. In a young mouse, as a hypothetical example, stem cells would quickly get to work rebuilding muscle tissue if its hindlimb had been injured taking too many spins on a wheel. However, if the muscle tissue in this same young mouse were exposed to old blood, the signal pathways designed to give the local stem cells the green light to jump into repair mode would be blocked.[130]

What do their findings about the pro-aging factors in old blood mean for longevity research? To begin, it means

129 Justin Rebo, et al., "A Single Heterochronic Blood Exchange Reveals Rapid Inhibition of Multiple Tissues by Old Blood," *Nature Communications* 7, no. 1 (2016).

130 Ibid.

Countess Báthory's approach of transfusing young blood would likely prove futile in clinical settings. Youthful blood would be overpowered by the high level of pro-aging proteins in an elderly recipient's blood, and it is unlikely the patient would see any significant improvement in the elasticity of their skin or texture of their hair.

Instead, the Conboys are working on a filtering system that would remove the inhibitory proteins in an individual's old blood so that stem cells could once again receive the instructional chemical signals they did in an individual's youth. This method would avoid the risks of the potentially unethical uses of "blood boys," as seen in HBO's series *Silicon Valley*.

Dr. Irina explains that transfusions from so-called "blood boys" are not a feasible solution because old individuals do not have genetically identical younger twins. This would be necessary to undergo high-volume and repeated blood transfusions throughout our later years. Without genetically identical blood, those undergoing transfusions are at a high risk of suffering from the transfer of pathogens or autoimmune diseases. Current treatments for eliminating pathogens often have the negative side effect of killing healthy proteins circulating in the blood, and, thus, potential rejuvenation benefits from the young blood would be negated.

But despite the realities realized in the lab, enduring beliefs in the alleged healing properties flowing through the blood of the young has compelled some biohackers and individuals desperate to reclaim their health to spend $8,000 for blood transfusions at companies such as Ambrosia.[131] And eerily reminiscent of the legend of Countess Báthory, it is said the late North Korean dictator Kim Il-sung ordered his doctors to inject him with syringes of blood from young virgins, believing it would allow him to live and rule until he was 120 years old. Perhaps unsurprisingly, the now-deceased leader referred to himself as the "Eternal President."[132]

In theory, an individual seeking this treatment would go to a clinic and undergo a process called apheresis. In this FDA-approved procedure, blood is drawn from a patient and then filtered to remove harmful properties. Today, this mechanism is most often used to remove antibodies that cause an autoimmune disease. The same process could potentially be adapted for a patient looking to rejuvenate their body and delay the onset of age-related diseases except that instead of removing antibodies, the blood would be filtered to eliminate pro-aging proteins, cancerous cells, and senescent cells. The Conboys say just one apheresis treatment could yield results.

The Conboys are currently working in partnership with longtime apheresis expert Dr. Dobri Kiprov to develop a treatment. But like their aging research peers, without aging earning recognition as a treatable condition from the FDA, the only current available route to clinical validation is to address the symptoms of aging.

---

131 Erin Brodwin, "A Controversial Startup That Charges $8,000 to Fill Your Veins with Young Blood Now Claims to Be Up and Running in 5 Cities across the US," *Business Insider*, 2019.

132 Damien Gayle, "North Korean Dictator Kim Il-Sung Thought Transfusions of Blood from Youths Would Help Him Live to 100," *The Daily Mail*, 2014.

These could include sarcopenia, osteoporosis, neurodegeneration, inflammatory and fibrotic diseases, and metabolic diseases, such as Type II diabetes, liver adiposity, and fibrosis, says Dr. Irina.

The Conboys could also potentially use the framework of the TAME trial—testing the treatment's effectiveness in treating a bundle of age-related diseases—as a potential route through the FDA.

But for now, Dr. Irina warns, "Do not inject yourself with other people's body fluids—you do not know what is being put into you."[133]

---

133 Angela Chen, "Everything Wrong with the Young Blood Injection Craze," *The Verge*, 2019.

CHAPTER 12

STEM CELL EXHAUSTION

Stem cells are critical to replenishing old cells and maintaining the health of our tissues. As we age, stem cell activity declines due to age-related issues, including cellular senescence. Without a healthy, active supply of stem cells our tissue function declines—leading to frailty and many age-related ailments.

Our bodies are full of cells. In fact, human beings, with all of our complexities—from our internal organs, the color of our skin, and the brain matter that controls our thoughts— are all the result of genetic information encoded in cells. If you are an average person, you are made up of roughly 37.2 trillion cells, according to some estimates. Our cells, put simply, are the raw material and building blocks of our body.[134]

---

134 Rose Eveleth, "There Are 37.2 Trillion Cells in Your Body," *The Smithsonian Magazine*, 2013.

Not all cells are created equal. They were designed to perform a specific function, to fulfill a particular purpose. Our heart cells create the tissue and muscles that allow this vital organ to pump the blood that flows throughout our body. Our epidermal cells create the protective barrier between our insides and threats from the outside world. Our bone cells makeup the skeletal frame that keeps us upright, and our muscle cell varieties form the fibers that allow our limbs to climb stairs or perform a set of bicep curls. In complex organisms such as humans, there are believed to be roughly 200 cell types, each catering to a different bodily need.[135]

Unfortunately, simply living and breathing causes significant damage to the cells that give us life and movement. Some individuals' behavior creates more cellular injury than others. Luckily, we have built-in cellular repair mechanisms that keep us above the ground and allow us to still engage in activities contrary to our doctor's advice. A college student, for example, who undergoes four years of alcohol-filled extracurricular activities relies heavily on liver cells to repair the damage cheap beer and vodka has incurred on their body.

Cellular repair and maintenance are also critical for behavior that is generally positive for our overall health. A marathoner depends on cellular repair to recover from a tissue-damaging interval workout and to build the muscle fibers that will eventually give them the endurance and strength to cross the finish line.

---

135 Jacquelyn Cafasso, "How Many Cells Are in the Human Body? Fast Facts," *Healthline*, 2018.

But perhaps the most damaging circumstance of all is the passing of time. As we age, our tissues begin to breakdown and our immune system weakens. For these reasons, we rely on a very special class of cells that give life to new cells—stem cells.

Unlike other cells throughout our body, stem cells can divide and renew themselves for extended periods of time and give rise to different cell types. However, when our stem cells stop dividing, our body can no longer mend itself. Thus, stem cell exhaustion is believed to be one of the leading causes of aging.[136] While this depletion of stem cells leaves us old, frail, and sick, treating damaged areas with stem cell therapies has the potential to dramatically improve medical conditions or even make us "young" again.

But these are still just potential therapies. While an increasing number of stem cell treatments have entered the clinical trial process, very few are currently available for medical use, the most prevalent being blood stem cell transfusions used in post-cancer treatments or for blood or immune system diseases. Treatments currently trying to gain FDA approval could take a decade or longer to work through the trial process if they prove safe and effective.

STEM CELL TYPES

To understand both the possibilities of stem cell therapies as well as the complexities and mysteries that have stalled scientific progress, it is important to grasp the different stem

---

136 López-Otín, 1194-1217.

cell types, the role they play in the body, and how scientists can manipulate them for medical purposes.

There are three categories of stem cells: Adult (or somatic) stem cells, embryonic (or pluripotent), and most recently, induced pluripotent stem cells (iPSCs).

When adult stem cells divide, they can give birth to an identical unspecialized adult stem cell, or it can produce cells of a particular type that carry out a specific function. Depending on the location of the adult stem cell, the new cells could be red blood cells, nerve cells, skin cells, and so on. These cells then work to undertake their special task and oversee any maintenance or reparative needs of their assigned location, whether in the pancreas, gut, or brain. With a keen awareness of the well-being of its surrounding tissue, adult stem cells will often remain dormant until additional cells are needed to see to standard upkeep requirements or meet increased reparative demands due to disease or injury. Whether it is the hungover college student or a marathoner training for a big race, the longevity and efficiency of our tissues and organs are critically dependent on our adult stem cells and their ability to continue producing new, healthy cells.

Human embryonic stem cells are derived from the place in which they get their name—early human embryos. When the embryo is just in its first few days of life, it is composed of a clump of roughly 150 total cells. This is called the blastocyst. During embryo development, this tiny ball of great human potential will ultimately produce the cells necessary to help us grow through each trimester and eventually mature into adulthood. This tremendous growth can occur since embryonic stem cells, unlike adult stem cells, are pluripotent—capable of creating any of the more than 200 cell types in the human body. For scientific use, embryonic stem cells are largely taken from embryos of eggs that have been donated with consent and were fertilized in vitro. In the lab, these pluripotent stem cells can propagate new sister cells indefinitely, as well as continue to give rise to any cell type in the body. However, controlling what cell variety an embryonic stem cell creates is a lingering major hurdle scientists are still working to overcome.[137]

Researchers first discovered methods to extract embryonic stem cells from young mouse embryos back in 1981, and for several decades thereafter, scientists largely used embryonic stem cells and adult stem cells in their research. However, in 2006, a failed orthopedic surgeon turned scientist uncovered mechanisms to manipulate and reprogram adult cells to have the pluripotent powers of embryonic stem cells. These are known as iPSCs.[138]

THE YAMANAKA FACTORS

In 1987, Shinya Yamanaka was a resident at the National Osaka Hospital in Osaka, Japan. There, he attempted to perform the first surgery of his very short-lived surgical career. As Dr. Yamanaka recounts the story, it took the young Yamanaka over an hour to try and fail at a simple surgery a more capable surgeon could have completed in ten minutes.

137 "Introduction: What Are Stem Cells, and Why Are They Important?" *National Institutes of Health*, accessed June 4, 2020.

138 "The Promise of Induced Pluripotent Stem Cells (Ipscs)," *The National Institutes of Health*, accessed June 4, 2020.

His shortcomings in the operation room earned him the name "Jamanaka," a pun for the word "jama," which means "obstacle" in Japanese.[139]

In addition to losing confidence in his potential to be a successful medical doctor, Dr. Yamanaka was disheartened by the realization that many of the patients cared for at the hospital had incurable diseases. This included his father, who succumbed to Hepatitis C before treatment was available for the virus.

The passing of his father, as well as treating other sick patients whom he knew would meet a similar fate, left Dr. Yamanaka feeling he could do more good by focusing his work on a different area of the medical field.

"Painful and unforgettable bedside experiences finally drove me to switch my goal from becoming a surgeon who would help free patients from pain to becoming a basic scientist who would eradicate those intractable diseases by finding out their mechanisms and ultimately a way of curing them," Dr. Yamanaka explained in an interview with the Nobel Foundation.[140]

To the eventual great fortune of his career, and to the rest of humanity, Dr. Yamanaka decided to leave his work as a practicing doctor for other, more research-oriented pursuits and began working on his PhD.

139 Robert Balza Jr., "The Holy Grail of Medicine–A Look at Ethical Stem Cell Research," *Christian Life Resources*, accessed June 4, 2020.
140 "Shinya Yamanaka Biographical," *The Nobel Prize Foundation*, accessed June 4, 2020.

He first began working with stem cells during his postdoctorate work at the Gladstone Institute for Cardiovascular Diseases in San Francisco. Embryonic mouse stem cells were a tool used in his research, but eventually became his main interest and the subject of his scientific endeavors when he returned to Japan.

The research climate in the lab he worked in back home lacked the same energy he experienced in America. After excessive amounts of time cleaning mice cages and little time spent on meaningful research concerning stem cells, Dr. Yamanaka became depressed and strongly considered returning to the medical profession.

However, his luck turned around in 1999 when he earned a position as an assistant professor at the Nara Institute of Science and Technology (NAIST). The job gave him the freedom to focus on the research area of his choice, which he determined would be to find a solution to the hurdles in embryonic stem cell (ESC) research at the time. Most researchers working with ESCs spent their time studying how the cells differentiated into the various cells in the body. This posed several problems.

One, ethical concerns regarding the use of ESCs in the US and Japan made gaining access to the cells difficult. And two, there was a risk of the immune system rejecting the cells when they were removed from cultures created in the lab and injected into the body. To overcome these obstacles, Dr. Yamanaka decided on a bold and perhaps foolishly ambitious goal for his team. He would use nuclear reprogramming to create ESC-like pluripotent cells derived from adult cells, avoiding the controversial use of embryos and, he hoped, the risk of immune system rejection.

In 2006, now a professor at Kyoto University, Dr. Yamanaka shocked the scientific world by achieving what he had set out to do seven years prior. He and his team published a paper in the journal *Cell* detailing how they had used four genes, which became known as the "Yamanaka factors," to induce pluripotency in adult cells taken from mice.

In other words, they reengineered regular, non-reproducing adult cells to become ESC-like cells that could become any cell type in the body. He called these lab-made creations iPSCs. The following year in November 2007, Dr. Yamanaka generated iPSCs in human adult cells.

With Dr. Yamanaka's discovery, the scientific world was infused with newfound energy and optimism about the potential of groundbreaking developments in regenerative medicine. If the promises of iPSCs held true, they could be the vehicle that enabled the scientific community to overcome two major roadblocks that had hampered advancements in stem cell therapies. By removing the ethical concerns surrounding the use of ESCs and the danger of immune system rejection when using adult stem cell therapies, iPSCs could provide scientists with a tool that would lead to a great leap in cell-based treatments. For these reasons, Dr. Yamanaka was awarded the Nobel Prize in Medicine in 2012.[141]

---

141 Ibid.

Now, thirteen years after Dr. Yamanaka first published his paper in *Cell*, iPSCs have indeed been a great tool for drug development and have provided a better option than animal cells for modeling diseases. However, they have not yet replaced the need for donated organs for transplants or been used to regrow or mend damaged tissue in human patients on a wide scale. These goals may still be realized, but more research is needed before scientists are capable of manipulating iPSCs to form the desired cell type and be transplanted without risking patients' health.[142]

POTENTIAL APPLICATIONS OF CELL-BASED THERAPIES

For the 114,000 Americans waiting in line for a life-saving organ transplant, progress in stem cell research and the development of treatments has been painfully and, in many cases, fatally slow.[143] It is a tragic case of supply versus demand. For liver transplants alone, twenty thousand individuals in America are on the waiting list, but only around five thousand transplant operations happen per year.[144] For those waiting for a liver, there must first be a death to save their own life. There are also thousands of others whose liver disease is deemed too advanced for them to even warrant a spot on the transplant list.

142 "The Promise of Induced Pluripotent Stem Cells (Ipscs)," *The National Institutes of Health*, accessed June 4, 2020.
143 "Facts and Myths," American Transplant Foundation, accessed January 20, 2020.
144 Mike Yeomans, "Lygenesis Out to Prove the Age of Organ Regeneration Has Arrived," *University of Pittsburgh Innovation Institute*, accessed June 4, 2020.

Many of the researchers attempting to address the dire problem of organ shortages have focused their efforts on growing tissues in the lab, 3D printing, or manipulating animal organs to make them functional for human patients. Stem cell researcher Dr. Eric Lagasse wondered if a body suffering from liver disease was given the right materials, would it be able to heal itself?

Dr. Lagasse set out to test this thought in his lab at The University of Pittsburgh's McGowan Institute for Regenerative Medicine.

He began by injecting mice suffering from liver disease with healthy liver cells at different locations. He tried implanting the cells under their skin. The mice died. He tried the kidney. They died. He tried the abdominal cavity. He waited, fully suspecting the same unfortunate fate of all the previously treated mice. But this time the mice did not die. Instead, they gained weight, had increased energy levels, and their overall health appeared to be restored. Seemingly cured of their liver disease, they kept on living.[145]

The question was now "why"?

Dr. Lagasse discovered that the healthy liver cells had nestled their way into lymph nodes residing in the mice's abdominal cavity. Typically, lymph nodes serve as an "organ for the immune system," activating the helper T-cells that rush to the rescue when we catch the flu or any type of virus or infection.

---

145 Michael Hufford, "Dean Kamen—Dean of Invention—Lygenesis Overview," 2017, Video,

But to Dr. Lagasse's great surprise, the lymph nodes, acting as an incubator and bioreactor, provided a fertile environment for the liver cells to proliferate and eventually transform the lymph nodes themselves into mini blood-filtering livers.

The visual of free-floating mini livers may seem bizarre, but some organs, including the liver and thymus, can carry out much or even all of their functions—whether located in the arms, legs, abdominal region, or in their original location.

"We're talking about bioreactors that could grow any number of tissues inside the body," Dr. Lagasse explained to Discover Magazine. "This could work for any organ that secretes things or produces cells."[146]

The unexpected results of Dr. Lagasse's experiment eventually led to the founding of LyGenesis. The organ regeneration company aims to prove, as shown in Dr. Lagasse's mice experiment, that lymph nodes can be appropriated to grow operational miniature ectopic organs in humans. If successful, doing so could create a significant new therapeutic option for the growing number of individuals either ineligible for a transplant due to comorbid medical conditions or who are waiting in a never-ending line for a new organ. For some, the lymph node-made organs could serve as an intermediary before a patient's turn to receive a transplant, and for others, replace the need for a donated organ altogether.[147]

---

146 "Big Idea: Turning Lymph Nodes into Liver-Growing Factories," Discover, 2012.
147 Ibid.

LyGenesis's approach also addresses several of the leading impasses in stem cell research. While labs have successfully isolated and grown stem cells in a petri dish, humans have not yet overcome Mother Nature's own self-determination when foreign, lab-bred stem cells are placed into a body. Once the cells are taken from the controlled, glass-protected lab environment and injected into an endlessly complex, highly regulated ecosystem of the human body, there is no telling how the stem cells may differentiate. What was once a thriving cell living in the confinement of a glass dish may become a rogue cell once let lose in a patient.

Paulo Fontes, MD, chief medical officer at LyGenesis, has seen this through his own work with stem cells: "The cell that you have in a petri dish in your lab looks great, but the moment you put it into a live body, the cell will take its own course and differentiate into something that you do not control."

If proven effective and safe, the LyGenesis approach would also tackle the key issue of "vascularization"—the ability for an organ to connect with vessels that carry blood once it is placed in a living body. This is currently a mechanical hurdle that has yet to be addressed by researchers attempting to grow or print whole organs in labs.

LyGenesis is set to begin phase 2 of clinical trials in 2020, meaning their treatment will be tested in human patients. With the clear and recognized target of treating end-stage liver disease, the company has not needed to wait for dramatic changes in policy to pursue their regenerative therapy.

"Unlike other folks that are trying to target aging itself, we are targeting some of the breakdowns associated with aging that have far more regulatory precedent," explains LyGenesis CEO Michael Hufford, PhD.

With a background in clinical development and previous experience engaging with the FDA, Dr. Hufford's and his team's choice of disease was made with the understanding of how the FDA operates: "We have tried to pick an approach with a lot of precedent for engaging the FDA as a cell-based therapy. Our lead indication is for patients with end-stage liver disease. You do not have to convince anyone at the FDA that is a critically important patient population."

With the extensive damage modern Americans inflict on their livers through poor lifestyle choices, liver disease, in particular, is a major threat to the home front.

For every one person on the liver transplant waiting list, ten are too sick to even qualify for a spot on the ledger.

The LyGenesis team believes their approach will work to close the fatal gap between organ supply and demand. If proven correct in human studies, the cells taken from one donated healthy liver could treat dozens of patients as opposed to the one lucky patient who currently benefits when a donated liver becomes available.

In theory, the procedure itself would be significantly less daunting, less expensive, and safer than current high-risk organ transplant operations.

As Dr. Hufford has previously described with the outlet Longevity Technology, the procedure would not be much more than a brief trip to the hospital.

"The patient would be put under light sedation, the endoscope would be moved into a place where it can access your lymph nodes—the mesentery, in your abdominal region—and thirty minutes later you'd have multiple ectopic cell clusters placed there, engrafted by a cellular therapy, and you'd potentially even be able to leave the same day," he envisions.

Then, "Over the course of the next few weeks and months, your lymph nodes would serve as bioreactors to grow multiple ectopic organs—a process called 'organogenesis'—that would begin filtering your blood and providing life-saving support."[148]

While liver disease is the lead disease indication in the pipeline, the same method could be potentially be used to treat an ailment we all suffer from as we grow older—a weakened immune system. LyGenesis is currently testing whether the lymph nodes could work as bioreactors to regenerate the thymus—a key regulator in immune system health. This treatment could serve as a disease intervention, strengthening the production of the T-cells necessary to protect us from infections as well as slowing the onset of age-related, chronic conditions. Other therapeutic targets with proof of concept in small animal studies include kidney and pancreas regeneration.

---

148 Ben Turner, "Exclusive Profile: Lygenesis and Growing Ectopic Organs," *Longevity Technology*, accessed June 4, 2020.

The surprise discovery that resulted from Dr. Lagasse's original mice experiment still sounds like part of a plot from the pages of a novel set far into the future, but the studies are published in the journal *Nature BioTechnology*, not in the latest science fiction book.

The key to novel, industry-changing discoveries such as his, says Dr. Lagasse, is giving scientists the freedom to explore ideas.

Dr. Yamanaka's discovery of iPSCs is an even more spectacular example, he says: "Yamanaka got his Nobel Prize because he found a student that was willing to do a crazy experiment that everyone else thought was hopeless."

But the liberty of exploration is only possible when you have the means to do so. Scientists live and die by grant money, explains Dr. Lagasse, and the current system does not award scientists who are trying to explore something innovative, something with unanswered questions.

Dr. Lagasse eventually received grant funds to study the possibilities of ectopic livers, but only after multiple, time-consuming attempts of rewriting rejected grant proposals.

"The system at the moment is broken," he says. "When you are not stressed about money and your brain can think about all of the different approaches you could try, that is how you can get a big jump and discover something."

CHAPTER 13

EPIGENETIC ALTERATIONS

Epigenetic alterations are negative changes in gene expression that compromise our cells and result in accelerated aging and age-related diseases.

Nature versus Nurture. This phrase was popularized by the polymath Sir Francis Galton in 1869 after he read the pioneering work of his half-cousin, Charles Darwin. In the first chapter of Darwin's *The Origin of Species,* he detailed his observations about variation within populations. These findings intrigued Galton. He became determined to investigate the question of whether it was an individual's parents and relatives, or the community in which they resided, that had a greater impact on who they became.[149]

---

149 David Burbridge, "Francis Galton on Twins, Heredity and Social Class," *The British Journal For the History of Science* 34, no. 3 (2001): 323-340.

But while Galton is credited with coining the phrase, and less impressively the concept of eugenics, the question of whether a person's traits are passed down through inheritance or are shaped by environmental factors dates back to at least 400 BCE when Hippocrates and ancient physicians and philosophers debated the dominance of one factor over the other.[150]

NATURE VERSUS NURTURE

Several millennia later, scientists have attempted to answer the age-old question of nature versus nurture by studying identical twins separated at birth.

Identical twins are the result of one fertilized egg that splits into two. As the term indicates, these twins are indeed identical, sharing 100 percent of the same genes. Their genetic homogeneity makes them ideal test subjects to weigh competing theories of our genome's and our environment's influence on our lives.[151]

Over time, numerous studies have analyzed identical twins separated at birth. Researchers have profiled brothers such as Jim Lewis and Jim Springer. The two siblings were adopted by different families three weeks after birth and were not reunited until they were thirty-nine years old. Despite nearly forty years of having never met, their life paths had remarkable similarities. Both their first

---

150 "Nature vs. Nurture Theory (Genes vs. Environment) Center," *MedicineNet,* Last modified July 25, 2017.

151 Jordana T. Bell, et al., "A Twin Approach to Unraveling Epigenetics," *Trends in Genetics* 27, no. 3: (2011): 116-125.

and second wives shared the same names, first Linda and then Betty. Both men named their first child James Allen, excelled in similar subjects in school, drove a Chevrolet, smoked heavily, and even vacationed at the same Florida beach.[152]

One would imagine that their identical genomes must have played a dominant role in their uncanny similarities.

But while the striking parallels between the lives of the Jims appear to be a home run for team nature, looking at twin studies from a micro-level perspective tells a more complex story.

A 2015 report published in the journal *Nature Genetics* analyzed twin studies conducted over the previous fifty years, determining that variation in human traits and diseases were 49 percent the result of genetics and 51 percent a result of environmental influences.

So to answer the question that has stirred the minds of ancient philosophers and Darwin's kin, both nature and nurture play a role in the reflection we see in the mirror.

But how do identical twins, who share roughly twenty thousand genes, develop different behavioral and physical traits and diseases throughout their lives?

The answer is epigenetics.

---

152 Edwin Chen, "Twins Reared Apart: A Living Lab," *The New York Times*, December 9, 1979.

OUR EPIGENOME AND GENE EXPRESSION

Epigenetics is the study of how those twenty thousand genes are expressed. Every cell in every individual has the same genome. Our genome has all the genetic information our cells need to perform the countless processes and functions happening throughout the body. But with all that information, how do our cells determine which intelligence to use and which to ignore? That is the job of our epigenome.

Although every cell has the genetic information to potentially become a liver cell, we could not live if all of our cells decided to differentiate into liver cells. We also need cells to make our eyes, heart, lungs, brain, lymph nodes, and so on. Epigenetic markers—beginning at the time we are first developing in the womb—are the maestro telling the cells throughout our bodies what to become and what to do. The epigenome does this by switching on or switching off the correct set of genetic instructions for each cell type to read.

Unlike our genome, our epigenome is not fixed. As we mature or face new circumstances, be it going on a vegan diet or enduring a period of high stress, our epigenome may turn on or turn off or enhance or reduce the expression of certain genes to best adapt to the situation.

And as has been shown in identical twins, our actions can have a negative or positive impact on our epigenome and induce the expression or suppression of certain genes. Smoking and other harmful behaviors, including a poor diet and a lack of exercise, damage our cells and can cause gene expressions that lead to cancer and other serious conditions.

One of the most detrimental impacts on our epigenome is the passing of time.

For example, as we age, malfunctions in methylation patterns—a process that strengthens or suppresses the expression of genes, among other age-related alterations—might impede our cells from accessing the information necessary to read signals from the epigenome and carry out their assigned duties. Cells become malfunctioning and eventually lose their identity.[153]

REMOVING THE RUST FROM OUR EPIGENOME

Dr. David Sinclair compares the age-related changes in our epigenome and the resulting information loss to a DVD or CD that has accumulated scratches over years of use.[154]

The data stored on the CD of Billy Joel's best hits is as it was the day it was first purchased, but the wear and tear on its surface is interfering with the ability of the CD player to clearly and fully read it. An older CD is not quite its younger self.

Dr. Sinclair believes that if the cellular deficiencies and malfunctions are largely a result of cells' inability to interpret information, then this problem could be resolved by returning stem cells to a younger state, i.e., before the build-up of biological rust and age-related epigenetic alterations—but

---

153 Ian Cowell, "Epigenetics–It's Not Just Genes That Make Us," *British Society for Cell Biology*, accessed June 5, 2020.

154 Sinclair, *Lifespan: Why We Age—and Why We Don't Have To.*

not so young that they lose their cellular identity and function.[155] The Billy Joel CD just needs some polishing.

Thanks to Nobel Prize winner Dr. Shinya Yamanaka's discovery of how to create iPSCs, scientists now know how to reverse cells back to an embryonic-like state. But as explained in the previous chapter, researchers currently cannot fully and dependably control the levers on what type of cell an iPSC ultimately becomes.

The company Turn Biotechnologies (Turn Bio) believes it has discovered a mechanism to work around this—a way to remove the scratches from the CD without losing information about the songs it contains.

Marco Quarta, PhD, is a co-founder and chief scientific officer of the company. As with Dr. Sinclair, Dr. West, Dr. Horvath, and others, Dr. Quarta had a fascination with aging from an unusually young age. His boyhood obsession did not come from a fear of death but, instead, from an interest in questions surrounding life.

"It was not that I discovered death and started to be concerned about it. It was more of the opposite. I started to discover life and was fascinated by it," he explains. "The idea of living long—the fact that there are different organisms living for different lengths of times. I did not think there was an obvious reason why we should age in the same way."

---

155 Ibid.

From the age of seven, as he recalls, he began his endeavor examining these questions around life and death in his makeshift garage lab. He did not find all the answers at his home in Bologna, Italy. But now, several degrees and a handful of decades later, Dr. Quarta believes he and his colleagues at Turn Bio have uncovered systems in nature that will get humans one step closer to being the masters of our own biological clock and healthspan.

The team at Turn Bio, as well as a separate group of researchers at the Salk Institute for Biological Studies, looked at what Dr. Yamanaka had accomplished with the four Yamanaka factors (known as OSKM), which induced the expression of genes that rejuvenated cells back to a pluripotent, embryonic-like state. To become "young" again, they knew that at some point throughout this transition, the elderly cells must have lost their epigenetic markers of old age.

Researchers at Turn Bio and Salk have discovered that the process of rejuvenation and the return to pluripotency occurs at separate stages when the Yamanaka factors are activated— meaning a blood stem cell, for example, will lose its epigenetic markers of age. It will become young again before it loses its cellular identity as a blood stem cell.[156]

This multi-step process is not surprising, says Dr. Quarta, because this is the way things work in nature as well. "Nature figured it out," he says.

---

156 Alejandro Ocampo, et al., "In Vivo Amelioration of Age-Associated Hallmarks by Partial Reprogramming," *Cell* 167, issue 7 (2016).

When we have children, we do not give birth to old babies, Dr. Quarta and others reason when attempting to explain this process of cell rejuvenation. The embryonic cells that become our children display all the markers of youth, despite coming from individuals often well into their mature years. Our cells manage to self-rejuvenate so that when a woman gives birth, the child comes out as an epigenetically young baby.

The question then is if we use the Yamanaka factors to induce rejuvenation, can we halt our cells on their journey back to pluripotency at the exact point when they have lost their epigenetic markers of an old cell, but have not lost their identity?

The answer is yes; it has been done.

Researchers at the Salk Institute were the first to do it. In December 2016, a Salk team led by Juan Carlos Izpisua Belmonte, PhD, published a paper in the journal *Cell* showing that when they induced the expression of the OSKM genes in skin cells of progeria mice for a short period, the cells sitting in the petri dish lost their epigenetic markers of age without erasing their identity as skin cells. After this success, they decided to try it in living mice.[157]

The results led to a significant finding in aging research.

As Salk noted in its release after the study, "Compared to untreated mice, the reprogrammed mice looked younger; their cardiovascular and other organ function improved and—most surprising of all—they lived 30 percent longer

---

157 Ibid.

yet did not develop cancer. On a cellular level, the animals showed the recovery of molecular aging hallmarks that are affected not only in progeria but also in normal aging."

"Our study shows that aging may not have to proceed in one single direction," Dr. Belmonte said when the Salk team published the study. "It has plasticity and, with careful modulation, aging might be reversed."[158]

Turn Bio ran a different study aimed at testing the same question—can you rejuvenate a cell without risking the loss of its identity and, thus, its function?

Again, the answer to this question was yes. Instead of using progeria mice, they studied naturally aged mice and eight different human cell types taken from subjects who ranged from ten to ninety years of age. In addition to using the Yamanaka factors, they also included several other mRNA reprogramming factors that have proven effective in inducing cellular rejuvenation.

In one of Turn Bio's studies, they took muscle stem cells from aged mice, rejuvenated them using their cocktail of transcription factors, and transplanted them back into the muscles of the mice. They found the strength or "force" of the muscles in the mice had been returned to that of a young mouse.

---

158 Alejandro Ocampo, et al. "Turning Back Time: Salk Scientists Reverse Signs of Aging," *Salk Institute for Biological Studies,* December 15, 2016.

"We are talking about 30 percent force induction," says Turn Bio cofounder Vittorio Sebastiano, PhD.

The results of their study also proved encouraging for humans. When muscle stem cells were removed from elderly patients and then treated using Turn Bio's batch of transcription factors, the cells were also rejuvenated to youthful levels without changing cell identity.

Importantly, they discovered a Goldilocks incubation period for each cell type.

"If we differentiate cells like fibroblasts and endothelial cells, we use four days; for chondrocytes, three days; and for muscle stem cells, we use two days," Dr. Sebastiano explained in an interview with LEAF.

He says, "This is actually part of the secret of finding the sweet spot, the empirical moment in time just before the point of no return where the cell is becoming partially reprogrammed but has not yet lost its identity."[159]

There is a shorter-term and longer-term vision for what this treatment could look like in the coming years, pending FDA approval.

In the shorter term, an elderly patient or just someone who needs a tune-up would have low functioning, old stem cells removed from a target area—let's say the liver. These cells

---

159 "An Interview with Prof. Vittorio Sebastiano of Turn.Bio," *Life Extension Advocacy Foundation*, April 4, 2020.

would be taken to a lab. There, the liver stem cells would be rejuvenated using Turn Bio's cocktail of transcription factors. Then the young, high-functioning stem cells would be transplanted back into the patient from the location where they were originally removed. The freshly engrafted cells would behave as they once did when they were in their prime and would, in theory, restore the patient's liver to a younger state.

In March 2020, Dr. Quarta and Dr. Sebastiano published in the journal *Nature Communications* the results of these studies conducted in their labs at Stanford University and at Turn Bio.[160]

The later, more aspirational goal is that the treatment could have a global rejuvenating effect on the entire body, and could be done without ever having to remove cells from a patient. This would require a delivery method that accounted for the various rejuvenation periods for each cell type. As Dr. Sebastiano noted, finding the sweet spot where a cell loses its markers of age, but before it forgets who it is, may be one period of time for a heart cell and another different one for blood cells.

Administering the treatment to each tissue type in the body in vivo is still an ambitious task with many challenging lingering questions and safety concerns, but Dr. Quarta believes it is only a matter of time until scientists find the answers. The experimentation to develop these treatments is happening as we speak in Turn Bio labs.

---

160 Sarkar, Tapash Jay et al., "Transient Non-Integrative Expression Of Nuclear Reprogramming Factors Promotes Multifaceted Amelioration of Aging in Human Cells," *Nature Communications* 11, no. 1 (March 2020).

Of course, mastering the science is not the only—or perhaps even the steepest—hurdle Turn Bio will have to overcome before this and similar treatments become available to the public.

"The current regulatory path is focused on curing conditions, not preventing them," says Dr. Quarta. "Currently, you have to choose one indication and prove that you can cure it."

Despite aging being a known driving factor in many disease conditions, Dr. Quarta explains, Turn Bio and other longevity biotech companies face the challenge of showing that targeting aging can be curative and preventative.

If Turn Bio, for example, conducted clinical trials using its technology to treat osteoarthritis and the trial proved successful, the therapy could then potentially be repurposed to reenter clinical trials to treat a different condition. As with other treatments or drugs, assuming Turn Bio's technology effectively treated the various target conditions, only those suffering from the specific diseases could receive the therapy, unless it was prescribed off-label.

With the average successful clinical trial taking twelve years and costing $19 million, both time and costs make moving through the federal system exceedingly difficult.[161]

---

161 Thomas J. Moore, et al., Moore, Thomas J., Hanzhe Zhang, Gerard Anderson, and G. Caleb Alexander, "Estimated Costs of Pivotal Trials for Novel Therapeutic Agents Approved by the US Food and Drug Administration, 2015-2016," *JAMA Internal Medicine* 178, no.11 (2016): 1451.

That is why, like many of his peers working in aging research, Dr. Quarta is holding out hope for the TAME trial.

Regardless of the outcome of the TAME trial, he says, "It would be the first step of targeting aging in clinical trials. It would create a first proof of concept that this is doable for the entire community."

Ultimately, TAME could work as a future framework for Turn Bio if the company enters clinical trials to use their therapy to treat aging as an indication.

The millennia-old question of whether we are products of our nature (genome) or our nurture (epigenome) has been answered. We are both. But when it comes to how long and how healthfully we live, it is becoming increasingly clear that, in most cases, our epigenome has the upper hand.

But given the opportunity, we humans may have the tools to manipulate the gears of our epigenetic clocks and move back time to a younger biological age.

PART 3

FINDING THE FOUNTAIN

CHAPTER 14

THE CONSEQUENCES OF LIVING LONGER

One of the byproducts of maintaining good health is the distinct possibility of living longer. Just like all living creatures, humans appear to have a certain finite, maximum lifespan. The Italian lifelong smoker Jean Calment is believed to have reached that number when she passed away in 1997 at 122 years and 164 days. She maintained good health throughout her life, and finally quit smoking when she reached "retirement" age at 117.[162]

What if the experimental treatments discussed in this book and the many others being developed enable us all to live as long as Calment? Would world populations soar? Would Earth's resources be depleted? Would financial support programs for the elderly go bankrupt?

---

162 François Robin-Champigneul, "Jeanne Calment's Unique 122-Year Lifespan: Facts and Factors; Longevity History in Her Genealogical Tree," *Rejuvenation Research* 23 no.1 (February 17, 2020): 19–47.

These are some of the concerns integral to serious conversations about the potential impacts of increasing our lifespan, and are worthy of our attention.

OVERPOPULATION

Whether a healthier global population would also result in overpopulation is a question Bill and Melinda Gates have considered as they work on global health initiatives through the Bill and Melinda Gates Foundation.

They asked themselves, would saving lives lead to an overly crowded planet?[163]

Fortunately, their global health initiatives can continue free of that concern.

What they found aligns with reports published by leading international organizations, including the United Nations (UN).

Wealthier and healthier nations tend to have fewer children. A report released by the UN demonstrated this trend, showing that since the 1960s, the rate of the world population growth has been steadily declining. According to the UN's calculations, growth is expected to plateau in the year 2100. This would leave Earth with roughly 11 billion human inhabitants. There are currently 7.8 billion of us.[164]

---

163 Bill Gates and Melinda Gates, "10 Tough Questions We Get Asked," *Gates Notes* (blog), February 13, 2018.

164 "United Nations, Department of Economic and Social Affairs, Population Division," *World Population Prospects: The 2015 Revision, Volume II: Demographic Profiles*, accessed June 27, 2020.

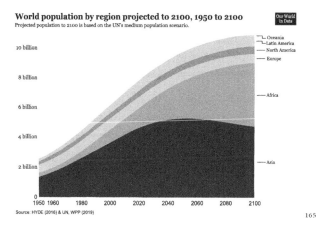

World population by region projected to 2100, 1950 to 2100
Projected population to 2100 is based on the UN's medium population scenario.

Source: HYDE (2016) & UN, WPP (2019)

165

While regions of Africa are still expected to see population growth after 2100, populations are actually expected to decline in ninety countries, including in two-thirds of Europe.

Nearly 11 billion humans, whose circumferences are growing increasingly larger, will take up additional space on the planet. Can Earth handle it?

The short answer is yes. There is enough landmass available to house the world population in 2100. However, depending on where an individual resides, the amount of property and space available to them may be impacted.[166] With traditional in-office working centers going out of fashion, individuals who can work remotely may choose to leave urban centers for the more spacious countryside.

---

165 Max Roser, et al., *World Population by Region Projected to 2100, 1950 to 2100*, Our World Data, Figure.

166 Richard Gray, "How Can We Manage Earth's Land?" *BBC*, June 29, 2017.

However, successful adaptation to the population growth over the next century will require behavioral changes from individuals living in wealthy countries.

"It is not the number of people on the planet that is the issue— but the number of consumers and the scale and nature of their consumption," David Satterthwaite, a senior fellow at the International Institute for Environment and Development in London, told the BBC.[167]

Still, even if space permits, this leaves us with 11 billion mouths to feed. Where will we find the resources?

INSUFFICIENT RESOURCES

More than 820 million people around the globe are hungry. For the most part, these individuals live in Africa or Asia and are disproportionately women. Expectant mothers who are food insecure have a higher likelihood of giving birth to children with health defects, and continued malnourishment leads to stunted growth. This suffering is unacceptable. Fortunately, numerous governmental and private initiatives are working on making hunger a problem of the past.

For decades, these efforts, along with global economic growth and improvements in human rights laws, have chipped away at the number of hungry mouths. However, numbers began to rise again in 2015, and the upward trend has continued since then. In most circumstances, the lack of available

---

167 Ibid.

nutrition was a result of increased civil unrest and conflict, natural disasters, and economic downturns.

Tragically, the severe economic consequences of the global COVID-19 pandemic are only expected to exacerbate the uptick in food insecurity. But importantly, this spike does not reflect a deficiency in actual physical resources.[168]

In fact, a shocking number of individuals are consuming too many resources.

Nearly 30 percent of the world's population—roughly two billion people—are either overweight or obese.[169]

The obesity epidemic in America should make our jaws drop, or at least put down our forks.

A study out of Northwestern University concluded that by 2020, 83 percent of men and 72 percent of women will be overweight or obese. In this same year, 77 percent of men and 53 percent of women will either have diabetes or pre-diabetes.[170]

More is not always merrier when it comes to serving sizes. The overwhelming majority of Americans—and many individuals throughout the world—should focus on eliminating calories, not adding additional food to their plate.

---

168 "Goal 2: Zero Hunger," United Nations, accessed June 8, 2020.
169 Centers for Disease Control and Prevention, "Obesity and Overweight," Updated June 13, 2006.
170 "Obesity Projections Worse Than Terrorism Threat for Future—And We Can Do Something about It," *Women's Health Research Institute* (blog), accessed June 27, 2020.

But overeating is not the only behavioral issue deserving of our concern. Americans toss shameful amounts of food into the trash.

America is one of the world's worst offenders when it comes to wasting food. According to the United States Department of Agriculture (USDA), in the United States, "food waste is estimated at between 30 and 40 percent of the food supply. This estimate, based on estimates from USDA's Economic Research Service of 31 percent food loss at the retail and consumer levels, corresponded to approximately 133 billion pounds and $161 billion worth of food in 2010."[171]

On an individual level, this means each American wastes between 225–290 pounds of food per year. Our rejected food rotting in the abyss of mountainous landfills would be enough to feed two billion people annually.[172] That would fill the hungry stomachs of the 820 million currently suffering from food insecurity several times over.

But even if we find it within ourselves to take—and eat—only what we need, a world with eleven billion people will require a considerable number of available calories. If we rely on current farming and agricultural practices, the amount of space necessary to produce sufficient calories may exceed space available, assuming the current rate of demand continues. Luckily, agriculturists, scientists, entrepreneurs, and

---

171 "Food Waste FAQs," US Department of Agriculture, accessed June 8, 2020.

172 Zach Conrad, "Relationship Between Food Waste, Diet Quality, and Environmental Sustainability," *PLOS One,* April 18, 2018.

governments are already working on innovating around these problems.

By far, one of the leading challenges is reducing our reliance on livestock and farm animals for meat.

While we should temper our concerns about human population growth, the enduring spike in farm animal populations is alarming.

From 1996 to 2016, the number of cattle on farms increased by 44 percent — and the number continues to rise. As of 2020, there are approximately 94.4 million cows on US farmlands.[173] The number of chickens has grown even more, going from 4.4 billion in 1966 to an incredible 22.7 billion in 2016. Bacon has remained a staple of the American breakfast, and the increase in pig populations shows it. The number of pigs in America rose by 92 percent during the same time period, reaching 981 million in 2016.[174]

Unsurprisingly, the massive numbers of farm-raised animals take up a substantial amount of land—especially livestock. A report by the Food and Agriculture Organization of the United Nations found that "26 percent of the planet's ice-free land is used for livestock grazing, and 33 percent of croplands are used for livestock feed production."[175]

---

173 United States Department of Agriculture (USDA), National Agricultural Statistics Service (NASS), Agricultural Statistics Board, *Cattle* (January 31, 2020).

174 "Meat and Animal Feed," Agriculture at a Crossroads, accessed June 8, 2020.

175 "Livestock and Landscapes," The Food and Agriculture Organization of the United Nations, accessed June 8, 2020.

These future hamburgers are the greatest users of Earth's land resources.

But now, a beef patty's journey no longer has to commence with a living, polluting, and space-consuming cow. It can—and has been—birthed in a lab. Memphis Meats, Aleph Farms, Higher Steaks, Mosa Meat, and Meatable are some of the companies working on using animal cells to grow meat in a petri dish.[176] While the techniques are still being perfected, the hope is that, eventually, a meat connoisseur will be unable to taste the difference between grain-fed cattle and lab-grown beef. When this system is realized on a grand scale, the amount of available land will increase dramatically and the resources previously used to sustain and transport farm animals when they are alive and when they become meat or poultry can be reallocated for different purposes.

BANKRUPT GOVERNMENT PROGRAMS

We should be concerned about the insolvency of government programs, but looming bankruptcy will not wait until 2100; it will be here beginning this decade.

With the current system of treating the symptoms of aging, and not aging itself, health care costs will become crippling in the coming years.

---

176 Jonathan Shieber, "Lab-Grown Meat Could Be on Store Shelves by 2022, Thanks to Future Meat Technologies," *Tech Crunch* (blog), October 10, 2019.

When all Baby Boomers reach retirement age in 2030, one in five US residents will be sixty-five years old or older. This will mark the first time in American history that seniors will outnumber children.[177] Looking further into the future, the US Census predicts that by the year 2050, there will be 83.7 million individuals over the age of sixty-five, almost double from 43.1 million in 2012. With Medicare headed for insolvency by 2026 and Social Security by 2035, it is unclear how seniors will be cared for if our current approach to health care remains in place.[178]

This is a problem felt by countries across the globe, but America is not faring well compared to our allies and competitors.

While America is a world superpower, we are not the ideal place to grow old. As discussed throughout this book, Americans, on average, are overcome by a series of chronic, debilitating diseases by their mid or late sixties. When measured against comparable countries, the US is lagging behind in the health outcomes of its mature populations.

The longevity-focused analytics company, Aging Analytics Agency, compiled an over three-hundred-page report ranking the US against the UK, Israel, the Netherlands, Switzerland, Spain, Singapore, Hong Kong, South Korea, Japan, China, and the European Union. The report scored countries according to their Health-Adjusted Life Expectancy (HALE). Out of the ten countries, the US came in dead last, behind

---

177 United States Census Bureau, "Older People Projected to Outnumber Children for First Time in US History," March 13, 2018.
178 Social Security, Status of the Social Security and Medicare Programs, "A Summary of the 2019 Annual Reports," 2019.

China. In other words, out of the countries studied, Americans live the fewest number of healthy years before disease takes over.

Health-Adjusted Life Expectancy vs. Life Expectancy

Health-Adjusted Life Expectancy, 2016	Country	Life Expectancy, 2016
76.2	Singapore	82.9
74.8	Japan	84.2
73.8	Spain	83.1
73.5	Switzerland	83.3
73.0	South Korea	82.7
72.9	Israel	82.3
72.1	Netherlands	81.6
71.9	United Kingdom	81.4
70.6	European Union	81.0
68.7	China	76.4
68.5	USA	78.5

179

Ironically, while America comes in last in HALE, the US has the highest per capita health care spending among developed countries at $9,892. Care for seniors consumes a disproportionate amount of our overall health care expenditures. In 2016, individuals of retirement age accounted for only 16 percent of the US population but were responsible for 36 percent of the total health spending.

The US's health expenditures are projected to grow at an average annual rate of 5.5 percent between 2018 and 2027, representing 19.4 percent of gross domestic product by 2027. Despite the projected increase in its health care spending,

---

179 Aging Analytics Agency, "National Longevity Development Plans: Global Overview 2019,"

the US is expected to take a further dive in life expectancy rankings by 2040—going from 43rd place to 64th—the largest decrease for a country defined as "high income." China's global ranking is expected to rise from 68th to 39th place.[180]

These predictions are not carved into stone. Our ability to remain a strong, healthy nation and to protect government programs that are the lifeline for the elderly in their later years depends on whether we choose to actually address what is bankrupting our country and compromising our well-being at its most fundamental level.

RIDING THE WAVES OF THE SILVER TSUNAMI

If we take steps to treat the aging process so that chronic diseases no longer steal the minds and bodies of our seniors, then we can reduce the disproportionate burden they place on our health care system. Instead, their wisdom and accumulated wealth can provide an economic opportunity.

"The Silver Tsunami brings with it many serious societal and economic challenges, but human will and ingenuity can refashion these challenges into opportunities. The social and economic ill consequences of an aging population can only be remedied in the long term by ensuring that while the numbers of elderly people increase, there is a corresponding increase in the age at which people remain healthy and productive," says Dmitry Kaminskiy, co-founder and managing partner at Deep Knowledge Ventures and author of *Longevity Industry 1.0.*

---

180 Ibid.

He elaborates: "In other words, the increase in Health-Adjusted Life Expectancy (HALE), the age up to which people are able to live relatively healthy lives, has to keep pace with the increase in life expectancy, to avoid the widening of the age bracket in which people are alive but unable to work productively, relying on the taxes and economic output of others in order to maintain their health and livelihood."

As Kaminskiy and others have argued, a more silver future can be a golden opportunity, but to avoid economic collapse, we must reconsider our retirement age.

With the anticipated collapse of pension programs in the near future, Americans must have this unavoidable conversation regardless of whether we have access to aging treatments or not.

***

As we consider the consequences of longer health—and perhaps lifespans—we must do so with the acknowledgment of current, unavoidable population trends.

Most notably, the world is growing older with or without treatments that target aging. Undoubtedly, this population shift presents novel challenges to our government programs and economy. If we had a choice, would we prefer this group to be healthy and productive, or sick and costly?

Issues concerning lack of space, depleted resources, and climate change must be addressed if we are to remain living and thriving on this planet in decades and centuries to come. But we must not fear these future threats through the lens of today.

This point is best cemented by peering back into our relatively recent history. Consider the exponential progress in science and technology over the past thirty or so years. If that short period could spawn the internet, social media, DNA sequencing, Google Maps, online shopping, magnetic resonance imaging (MRI), and smartphones, one can only imagine what the next fifty to one hundred years will bring.

CHAPTER 15

UNLOCKING BIOTECH'S POTENTIAL

———

The first time Americans learned the novel coronavirus disease 2019 (COVID-19) had crossed oceans and jumped borders to take a life of one of our own was on February 29, 2020. Although we would later learn of even earlier COVID-19-related deaths in California, the first reported fatality occurred in a Washington State nursing home located in the county where I grew up—just fifteen minutes away from my parents' home. It would be the first of seventeen confirmed deaths from the virus at Kirkland's Life Care Center, and just one of the over one hundred forty thousand in the United States and hundreds of thousands across the world. As I am writing this in July of 2020, the body count is still rising.[181]

There are many things we do not yet understand about this virus that has put our economies and many of our lives in

———

181 Derrick Bryson Taylor, "How the Coronavirus Pandemic Unfolded: A Timeline," *The New York Times*, June 9, 2020.

both a free fall and at a standstill. But one observation is absolutely and critically clear—if you are elderly or have an age-related chronic condition, the likelihood of dying from the virus increases significantly.

According to data collected by the CDC, individuals in their forties and younger have less than a 1 percent chance of dying from COVID-19. The likelihood of death falls as age decreases. However, when you point the arrow toward groups aged fifty and beyond, the bars on the chart begin to spasm and spike with each passing decade: an individual in their sixties has a 3.6 percent chance of fatality, an individual in their seventies has an 8 percent chance, and when someone turns eighty, the likelihood of death nearly doubles to 14.8 percent.[182]

While novel, COVID-19 is not unique in who it most impacts. Influenza acts in the same way. Out of the 61,099 individuals in the United States who died of influenza in the 2017–2018 season, 50,903 were aged sixty-five or older. This is not because the elderly neglect to get their annual flu shot. In fact, in that same influenza season, individuals aged sixty-five or older were approximately 20 percent more likely to be vaccinated than individuals aged fifty to sixty-four, and over 33 percent more likely to be vaccinated than individuals aged eighteen to forty-nine.[183] But vaccines cannot save a broken immune system.

---

182 Centers for Disease Control and Prevention, "Interim Clinical Guidance for Management of Patients with Confirmed Coronavirus Disease (COVID-19)," Updated June 2, 2020.

183 Centers for Disease Control and Prevention, "2017-2018 Estimated Influenza Illnesses, Medical Visits, Hospitalizations, and Deaths and Estimated Influenza Illnesses, Medical Visits, Hospitalizations, and Deaths Averted by Vaccination in the United States," Last modified November 22, 2019.

So as the world races to find a vaccine for COVID-19, we must recognize that even with the development of a vaccine, lives are still at risk. *The real antidote to COVID-19—and influenza—is youth.* The same medicine is the cure for the chronic-age related diseases that lead to widespread suffering, kill in masses, and bankrupt governments and families. It really is that simple.

***

As outlined at the beginning of this book, according to the CDC, the top ten indications for fatality in the US are the following in descending order: Heart disease, cancer, unintended injuries, chronic lower respiratory disease, stroke and cerebrovascular diseases, Alzheimer's disease, diabetes, influenza and pneumonia, kidney disease, and suicide.

These leading causes account for 74 percent of all deaths across the country.[184]

Aging is the greatest risk factor for eight of the ten, and, arguably due to their frailty, the elderly are more vulnerable to unintended injuries. The combined risk of fatality from these leading causes increase by 100 to 1,000 percent between the ages of thirty-five and eighty-five.[185]

---

184 Centers for Disease Control and Prevention, "Leading Causes of Death," Last modified March 17, 2017.

185 Kieth Comito, et al., "Aging Is the Foremost Risk Factor for COVID-19. Let's Fight It," *Life Extension Advocacy Foundation,* April 13, 2020.

The data could not be more transparent. If living a full and productive life is the goal, then the side-effects of aging are the undeniable enemy.

Over the past several decades in particular, we have made commendable progress toward building up our scientific arsenal of tools to combat the aging process. Throughout this book, we have discussed some of the scientists and entrepreneurs who have been working—often times under severe scrutiny—to discover and develop aging therapeutics.

Together, they are tackling the nine hallmarks of aging addressed in this book—telomere attrition, cellular senescence, genomic instability, loss of proteostasis, stem cell exhaustion, mitochondrial dysfunction, deregulated nutrient sensing, epigenetic alterations, and altered intercellular communications.

Among the stories about emerging aging science and treatments, you have learned about Oisín's senolytic technology that could rid our bodies of zombie-like toxin-producing senescent cells; LyGenesis and its development of free-floating endoscopic organs; and the Conboys' research on pro-aging factors in old blood and what we might do to clear them away. These are just a sample of the many—and growing number—of compelling and potentially life-changing research areas that concern the biology of aging.

A disproportionate percentage of the researchers mentioned in this book, and many others whose stories were not told on the preceding pages, risked their professional credibility for pursuing an area of science often perceived as unserious or fraught with quackery.

Dr. de Grey, biogerontologist and founder of the nonprofit Strategies for Engineered Negligible Senescence (SENS) Research Foundation, was one of the early longevity zealots who recognized aging to be one of the greatest ills facing humankind. For over twenty years, he has called on scientists and individuals or entities with the financial means to devote their brains or resources to combating the suffering that accompanies age-related cellular decline.

In those early days, Dr. de Grey's unorthodox view of aging as a solvable engineering problem was seen more as lunacy than prophecy.

He endured flagrant criticisms and name-calling by the scientific mainstream. Dr. de Grey's long beard and nonconformist lifestyle made him an easy target for scientists who tried to peg him as a mad scientist or a deranged narcissist seeking eternal life.

The shaming from his PhD peers spread from the corners of geriatrics to the wider biology circles when the MIT Technology Review published a profile of Dr. de Grey in 2005. The article chronicled his journey from working in artificial intelligence as an engineer to dropping that career path to become a biogerontologist intent on defeating aging. The magazine article outlined his intricate plan to fight biological decline.[186]

The over seven-thousand-word profile was met with such hostile disapproval from fellow scientists that the *Technology*

---

186 Nuland, Sherwin, "Do You Want to Live Forever?" *MIT Technology Review*, February 1, 2005.

Review responded with a challenge aimed at debunking Dr. de Grey's theories on the mechanisms of aging.

The editor of the magazine, Jason Pontin, wrote to readers at the time:

Technology Review is announcing a prize for any molecular biologist working in the field of aging who is willing to take up the challenge: submit an intellectually serious argument that SENS is so wrong that it is unworthy of learned debate, and you will be paid $20,000 if it convinces independent referees. In the case that even $20,000 is insufficient to motivate the relevant experts, we also invite contributions to the fund; anyone wishing to pledge should contact me.[187]

None of the submissions met the task of disproving Dr. de Grey's theories on aging.[188]

Now, fifteen years after the magazine described Dr. de Grey as potentially "nuts," the cover of the magazine in the August 2019 edition read, "Old Age is Over—if you want it." It then listed anti-aging drugs in its highly regarded "10 Breakthrough Technologies" of the coming year.[189]

The scientific and media mainstream must reassess their past skepticism and recognize the hard science that has

---

187 Jason Pontin, "The SENS Challenge," *MIT Technology Review*, July 28, 2005.
188 Jason Pontin, "Is Defeating Aging Only a Dream?" *MIT Technology Review*, July 11, 2006.
189 Gideon Lichfield, Editor's Letter: Old Age Is Over—If You Want It," *MIT Technology Review*, August 21, 2019.

been demonstrated in laboratories and has been detailed in countless peer-reviewed journal articles.

Of course, while journalists should not be determined to characterize aging researchers as fringe scientists, they must also be careful not to over-hype a treatment that has worked wonders in yeast, mice, or fruit flies. They are not humans. Only after successful human clinical studies can a researcher claim that his or her drug or treatment is safe and effective for human use.

However, the credibility aging researchers have earned is now attracting the attention of some investors who either see dollar signs or a chance at obtaining the one thing their money cannot currently buy—health in old age.

But support from the private sector has not been and likely will not be enough to provide researchers with the resources required to discover and develop treatments that will eventually extend our number of healthy, productive years.

Until more progress is made, children will continue to learn of their parents' or grandparents' perhaps avoidable terminal cancer diagnosis. Patients suffering from dementia will feel hopeless as they forget the names of their own children. A once active grandpa will be confined to a wheelchair for the rest of his days after suffering from a stroke. These are the everyday stories experienced by an endless number of Americans and individuals throughout the world. Each story has its own characters and plots, but they all have the same ending. By year's end, over two million Americans over the age of sixty-five will die—almost entirely as a result of age-related conditions.[190] These are not peaceful passings. They are marked by years of physical, emotional, and financial suffering that impacts far more than just the body in which the disease lives.

While unpleasant, we must indeed learn to accept some things in nature and in life.

Regardless of how much we love the light and warmth that emanates from the sun, the orange ball of hydrogen and helium will inevitably disappear over the western horizon each evening at dusk. And those who despise the cold cannot prevent the orbit of the Earth from turning summer into fall. The movements of the Earth and sun are systems that even the greatest minds in science and combined military forces in all the world's nations will never control, so we might as well learn to cope by saving up for a vacation to the tropics or a winter home in Florida.

But the cellular damage that occurs as we age is not governed by the same gravitational forces that spin the planets and stars. Not only can we influence it, but we have the true potential to control it.

As of this writing, the world has rallied together in an international effort to combat what mankind has identified as a universal enemy and threat to life.

The global response to the coronavirus is deserving of a term that has become widely overused: unprecedented.

---

190 Steven Schwartz, et al., "Deaths: Final Data For 2017," *National Vital Statistics Reports, Centers for Disease Control and Prevention, National Center for Health Statistic,* accessed June 27, 2020.

New York City, London, Madrid, Hong Kong, and virtually all of the world's biggest international business hubs have closed their storefronts, sacrificing billions in revenue. Schools and universities have gone virtual, with no clear indication in many places of when pupils will once again fill classrooms.

Since the outbreak of the coronavirus, US unemployment levels have gone from historic lows of 3.5 percent to levels that mirror jobless numbers during the Great Depression. So far, Congress has approved $6 trillion in spending in its effort to compensate for the economic damage the pandemic has caused businesses and families. [191]

While some businesses have become inoperative, others have changed their mode of operation to partake in the wartime-like effort to care for COVID-19-infected patients. General Motors (GM) has sidelined some of its automobile parts manufacturing and partnered with the ventilator company Ventec Life Systems to produce thirty thousand of the oxygen-giving machines. The US government has awarded GM and Philips a combined $1.1-billion-dollar contract to meet national and international demand for the machines.[192]

And the world has committed enormous resources to the search for a cure.

---

191 Andrew van Dam, "The US Has Thrown More Than $6 Trillion at the Coronavirus Crisis. That Number Could Grow," *Washington Post*, April 15, 2020.

192 David Shepardson, "GM, Philips to Supply 73,000 US Ventilators in $1.1 Billion Effort," *Reuters*, April 8, 2020.

In the US, the government rolled out Operation Warp Speed, which has directed $3 billion in appropriated dollars to fund the development of a vaccine. The FDA is overriding some of its stringent regulatory protocols and is working with drug companies to fast-track the clinical trial process to make a vaccine available to the public.[193]

Across continents, countries are enacting similar efforts, as universities and drug companies set aside their usual work and partake in the race to find a vaccine.

With some luck, a vaccine will be available within months of beginning clinical trials—an absolute record amount of time. With a safe and viable vaccine available, the world could seemingly return to normal operations even if the virus reappears in future seasons.

But again, while a vaccine may lessen the chances of death for vulnerable populations, it will not spare them from the suffering they are already experiencing from their frail bodies, weakened immune systems, and debilitating chronic diseases.

If we care about the same people dying of the coronavirus and all of humanity who will eventually become a member of a medically vulnerable population, then where is the outrage about and global response to the consequences of aging?

To end the suffering, we must treat the actual wound. We must acknowledge that the biological decline associated

---

193 HHS Press Office, "Trump Administration Announces Framework and Leadership for 'Operation Warp Speed,'" *US Department of Health and Human Services,* May 15, 2020.

with aging is the leading cause of death, pain, and suffering in America and across the world—and we must act on that indisputable truth.

The fight against cellular breakdown is deserving of the world's attention and much of our medical research dollars.

Similar to the $350 million in NIH dollars appropriated for Alzheimer's research for 2020,[194] or the hundreds of millions that have specifically been committed to developing cancer drugs, or the increase in funding that ultimately led to a treatment for AIDS, the US Congress has the power to appropriate dollars that are narrowly dedicated to furthering our understanding of the biology of aging and aiding in the development of the potential medical treatments that spring from that research.[195,196]

While meaningful and actionable progress has been made in aging research, the established science still only allows for a shallow understanding of the complete biology of aging. Without machines such as the submarine, humans could only guess which creatures roam at the bottom of the ocean floors.

And without sufficient resources—including the necessary dollars to provide for labs, personnel, and clinical trials—aging researchers cannot fully answer the lingering questions

---

194 "Alzheimer's Research Funding at the NIH," Alzheimer's Impact Movement, 2019.

195 "US Federal Funding for HIV/AIDS: Trends over Time," *Kaiser Family Foundation*, March 05, 2019.

196 George D. Demetri, "Public Funding Is the Lifeblood of Cancer Research," *Cancer Today*, December 21, 2018.

regarding the human biological aging process. The thousands of processes occurring in the human body do not function in a vacuum. They are like a complex puzzle or an ornate game of connect-the-dots, each uniquely shaped piece must fit, and the correct numerical corresponding lines must be drawn to get a full and accurate picture.

That is step one: Financing the scientists so they can uncover and develop the science.

And step two is cementing a better pathway to transport that science to translatable medicine available to the public. The TAME trial is a notable advancement toward creating a feasible route through the FDA for experimental aging drugs. Researchers, regulators, and other involved entities must continue to finesse the clinical trial process for a new class of aging therapeutics, and perhaps in the future agree on concrete biomarkers that will help serve as better indicators of the efficacy of experimental aging drugs.

But the preceding courses of action largely depend on—and can be expedited by—the public's recognition that aging is the number one risk factor for the chronic diseases and later-life frailty we suffer from. From that acknowledgment, the public must demand that their governing and regulatory bodies remove the barriers placed on aging research, support scientists investigating biology's hardest questions, and unlock biotech's potential to extend healthy lifespans.

The aim of fighting aging is not to escape death. It is to be *fully alive* during the one life that we were given. This is why we must hasten and strengthen our search to find the fountain.

APPENDIX

INTRODUCTION

- "Alzheimer's and Dementia Research: Alzheimer's Research Funding at the NIH." *Alzheimer's Impact Movement,* 2020. https://alzimpact.org/issues/research.

- Benedictow, Ole J., "The Black Death: The Greatest Catastrophe Ever." *History Today* 3, no. 5 (March 2005). https://www.historytoday.com/archive/black-death-greatest-catastrophe-ever.

- Center for Disease Control and Prevention. "Leading Causes of Death." https://www.cdc.gov/nchs/fastats/leading-causes-of-death.htm.

- "FY 2020 Program Descriptions." *National Institute on Aging.* Accessed June 27, 2020. https://www.nia.nih.gov/about/budget/fy-2020-justification-budget-request/fy-2020-program-descriptions.

- "The US Burden of Disease Collaborators. The State of US Health, 1990-2016: Burden of Diseases, Injuries, and Risk Factors Among US States." *JAMA* 319, no. 14 (April 2018): 1444–1472. https://jamanetwork.com/journals/jama/fullarticle/2678018.

PART 1: THE EVOLUTION OF LIFESPANS

CHAPTER 1: THE NEXT MEDICAL REVOLUTION

- Arias, Elizabeth, Jiaquan Xu, and Kenneth D. Kochanek. "United States Life Tables, 2016." https://www.cdc.gov/nchs/data/nvsr/nvsr68/nvsr68_04-508.pdf

- DeWitte, Sharon N. "Mortality Risk and Survival in the Aftermath of the Medieval Black Death." *PLOS One* 9, no. 5 (2014). https://journals.plos.org/plosone/article?id=10.1371/journal.pone.0096513.

- O'Neill, Aaron. "Child Mortality Rate (Under Five Years Old) in the United States, from 1800 to 2020*." *Statista*, 2019. https://www.statista.com/statistics/1041693/united-states-all-time-child-mortality-rate/#:~:text=Child%20mortality%20in%20the%20United%20States%201800%2D2020&text=The%20child%20mortality%20rate%20in,per%20thousand%20births%20in%201800.

- Orenstein, Walter A., and Rafi Ahmed. "Simply Put: Vaccination Saves Lives." *Proceedings of the National Academy of Sciences of the United States of America* 114, no. 16 (2017). https://doi.org/10.1073/pnas.1704507114.

- "Public Health Initiatives and Life Expectancy: Immunizations." *Regis College.* Accessed June 1, 2020. https://online.regiscollege.edu/blog/public-health-initiatives-life-expectancy-immunizations/.

- "The Black Death, 1348." *Eyewitness to History.* Accessed May 31, 2020. http://www.eyewitnesstohistory.com/plague.htm.

- "The Five Deadliest Outbreaks and Pandemics in History." *The Robert Wood Johnson Foundation,* 2013. https://www.rwjf.org/en/blog/2013/12/the_five_deadliesto.html.

- "United States of America—Under-Five Mortality Rate." *Knoema,* 2018. https://knoema.com/atlas/United-States-of-America/Child-mortality-rate.

CHAPTER 2: WHAT IS AGING?

- Aziz, Monowar, and Ping Wang. "What's New in Shock, May 2016?" *Shock (Augusta, Ga.)* 45, no. 5 (2016): 471. https://www.ncbi.nlm.nih.gov/pmc/articles/PMC4834889/.

- "DNA Methylation Grimage Strongly Predicts Lifespan and Healthspan." *Medical Xpress,* 2018. https://medicalxpress.com/news/2019-02-dna-methylation-grimage-strongly-lifespan.html.

- Fine, Andrea Nix, and Sean Fine. *Life According to Sam.* 2013; HBO Documentary Films. 2013.

- Fox, Margalit. "Sam Berns, 17, Public Face of a Rare Illness, Is Dead." *The New York Times*, January 13, 2014. https://www.nytimes.com/2014/01/14/us/sam-berns-17-public-face-of-a-rare-illness-is-dead.html.

- Gibbs, W. Wayt. "Biomarkers and Ageing: The Clock-Watcher." *Nature* 508, no. 7495 (2014): 168-170. doi:10.1038/508168a.

- Jazwinski, S. Michal, and Sangkyu Kim. "Examination of the Dimensions of Biological Age." *Frontiers in Genetics* 10 (2019): 263. doi:10.3389/fgene.2019.00263.

- Kolitz, Daniel. "A New Test Predicts When You'll Die (Give or Take a Few Years)." *Onezero*, January 23, 2019. https://onezero.medium.com/a-new-test-predicts-when-youll-die-give-or-take-a-few-years-2d08147c8ea6.

- López-Otín, Carlos, Maria A. Blasco, Linda Partridge, Manuel Serrano, et al. "The Hallmarks of Aging." *Cell* 153, no. 6 (2013). doi:10.1016/j.cell.2013.05.039.

- "What Is Aging?" *Life Extension Advocacy Foundation*. Accessed June 27, 2020. https://www.lifespan.io/aging-explained/.

- Wray, Britt. "The Ambitious Quest to Cure Ageing Like a Disease." *BBC*, 2018. https://www.bbc.com/future/article/20180203-the-ambitious-quest-to-cure-ageing-like-a-disease.

CHAPTER 3: ROADBLOCKS TO PROGRESS AND THE PATH FORWARD

- Bailey, Clifford J. "Metformin: Historical Overview." *Diabetologia* 60, no. 9 (2017): 1566-1576. doi:10.1007/s00125-017-4318-z.

- Benowitz, Steven. "Does NIA Spend Too Much on Alzheimer's?" *The Scientist*, February 19, 1996. https://www.the-scientist.com/news/does-nia-spend-too-much-on-alzheimers-58146.

- De Grey, Aubrey D. N. J. "TAME: A Genuinely Good Use of 75 Million Dollars." *Rejuvenation Research* 22, no. 5 (2019): 375-376. doi:10.1089/rej.2019.2274.

- "Discover Campaigns." *Life Extension Advocacy Foundation.* Accessed June 27, 2020. https://www.lifespan.io/campaigns/.

- "Dr. Nir Barzilai to Present at the 6th Aging Research for Drug Discovery Forum in Basel." *Insilico Medicine,* 2019. https://www.eurekalert.org/pub_releases/2019-03/imi-dnb031919.php.

- Dryden-Wustl, Jim. "NIH Funding Cuts Could Paralyze Drug Development." *Futurity*, November 19, 2017. https://www.futurity.org/nih-funding-drug-development-1608892-2/.

- Fleming, Alexander, G., Jennifer H. Zhao, Thomas C. Seoh, and Nir Barzilai. "A Regulatory Pathway for Medicines That Target Aging." *Public Policy & Aging Report* 29 no. 4 (2019): 128-133. doi:10.1093/ppar/prz018.

- Glossmann, Hartmut H., and Oliver MD, Lutz. "Metformin and Aging: A Review." *Gerontology* 65, no. 6 (2016): 581-590. doi:10.1159/000502257.

- Hill, Steve. "David Sinclair on NMN and Epigenetics." *Life Extension Advocacy Foundation*. September 10, 2019. https://www.lifespan.io/news/an-interview-with-dr-david-sinclair/.

- "ICD-11 for Mortality and Morbidity Statistics." International World Health Organization, 2018.

- Kaminskiy, Dmitry, Kate Batz, Franco Cortese, Ian Inkster, et al. "Metabesity and Longevity USA Special Case Study." *Aging Analytics Agency,* 2019. http://analytics.dkv.global/data/pdf/Metabesity/Full-Report.pdf.

- Kenny, Rose Anne, and Cathal McCrory. "Rebuking the Concept of Ageing as a Disease." *The Lancet* 6, no. 10 (2018): 768. doi:10.1016/S2213-8587(18)30266-3.

- Luke, Ake T., Austin Quach, James G. Wilson, Alex P. Reiner, et al. "DNA Methylation GrimAge Strongly Predicts Lifespan and Healthspan." *Aging (Albany NY)* 11, no. 2 (2019): 303. https://pubmed.ncbi.nlm.nih.gov/30669119/

- Meštrović, Tomislav. "Metformin History." *News Medical Life Sciences,* 2018. https://www.news-medical.net/health/Metformin-History.aspx.

- Moore, Thomas J., Hanzhe Zhang, and Gerard Anderson. "Estimated Costs of Pivotal Trials for Novel Therapeutic Agents Approved by the US Food and Drug Administration, 2015-

2016." *JAMA Internal Medicine* 178, no. 11 (2018): 1451-1457. doi:10.1001/jamainternmed.2018.3931.

- National Health Institute. "Nobel Laureates." October 15, 2019. https://www.nih.gov/about-nih/what-we-do/nih-almanac/nobel-laureates.

- Pace, Eric. "Roy Hertz, 93, Discoverer of a Cancer Treatment." *The New York Times*, 2002. https://www.nytimes.com/2002/10/31/us/roy-hertz-93-discoverer-of-a-cancer-treatment.html?auth=login-email&login=email.

- Schaffer, Regina. "Metformin May Hold Anti-Aging Promise to Increase 'Health Span.'" *Healio*, 2020. https://www.healio.com/news/endocrinology/20190829/metformin-may-hold-antiaging-promise-to-increase-health-span.

- Sinclair, David. *Lifespan: Why We Age—And Why We Don't Have To.* Atria Publishing Group. 2019.

- Sullivan, Thomas. "A Tough Road: Cost to Develop One New Drug Is $2.6 Billion; Approval Rate for Drugs Entering Clinical Development Is Less Than 12%." *Policy & Medicine*, 2019. https://www.policymed.com/2014/12/a-tough-road-cost-to-develop-one-new-drug-is-26-billion-approval-rate-for-drugs-entering-clinical-de.html#:~:text=%E2%80%9CPut%20another%20way%2C%20you%20need,drugs%20had%20actually%20been%20approved.

- "WHO Model List of Essential Medicines." *The World Health Organization*, 2015.

- Carrel, Alexis. "On the Permanent Life of Tissues Outside of the Organism." *Journal of Experimental Medicine* 15, no. 5 (1912): 516-528. https://www.ncbi.nlm.nih.gov/pmc/articles/PMC2124948/

- Cepelewicz, Jordanna. "Ingenious: Leonard Hayflick." *Nautilus*, 2016. http://nautil.us/issue/42/fakes/ingenious-leonard-hayflick.

- Hayflick, L., and P.S. Moorhead. "The Serial Cultivation of Human Diploid Cell Strains." *Experimental Cell Research* 25, no. 3 (1961): 585-621. doi:10.1016/0014-4827(61)90192-6.

- "Peyton Rous Biographical." *The Nobel Prize Foundation.* Accessed June 3, 2020. https://www.nobelprize.org/prizes/medicine/1966/rous/biographical/.

- Rasko, John, and Carl Power. "What Pushes Scientists to Lie? The Disturbing but Familiar Story of Haruko Obokata." *The Guardian*, 2015. https://www.theguardian.com/science/2015/feb/18/haruko-obokata-stap-cells-controversy-scientists-lie.

- "Medicine: Carrel's Man." *TIME*, 1935. http://content.time.com/time/magazine/article/0,9171,749033,00.html.

- "Medicine: Men in Black." *TIME*, 1938. http://content.time.com/time/magazine/article/0,9171,849014,00.html.

PART 2: HALLMARKS OF AGING

CHAPTER 5: TELOMERE ATTRITION

- Cooke, H.J., and B.A. Smith. "Variability at the Telomeres of the Human X/Y Pseudoautosomal Region." *Cold Spring Harbor Symposia on Quantitative Biology* 51, no. 0 (1986): 213-219. doi:10.1101/sqb.1986.051.01.026.

- "Elizabeth Blackburn: Nobel Prize in Physiology or Medicine 2009." *The Nobel Prize Foundation*, 2009. https://www.nobelprize.org/womenwhochangedscience/stories/elizabeth-blackburn.

- Harley, Calvin B., A. Bruce Futcher, and Carol W. Greider. "Telomeres Shorten During Ageing Of Human Fibroblasts." *Nature* 345, no. 6274 (1990): 458-460. doi:10.1038/345458a0.

- Jafri, Mohammad A., Shakeel A. Ansari, Mohammed H. Alqahtani, and Jerry W. Shay. "Roles of Telomeres and Telomerase in Cancer, and Advances in Telomerase-Targeted Therapies." *Genome Medicine* 8, no. 1 (2016): 69. https://pubmed.ncbi.nlm.nih.gov/27323951/

- López-Otín, Carlos, Maria A. Blasco, Linda Partridge, Manuel Serrano, et al. "The Hallmarks Of Aging". *Cell* 153, no. 6 (2013): 1194-1217. doi:10.1016/j.cell.2013.05.039.

- O'Connor, Clare. "Telomeres of Human Chromosomes." *Nature*, 2008. https://www.nature.com/scitable/topicpage/telomeres-of-human-chromosomes-21041/.

- Tapis, Fancy. *Cells Divide—Telomeres Shorten.* Image. https://www.shutterstock.com/image-illustration/cells-divide-telomeres-shorten-660503917.

- Tapis, Fancy. *Telomeres Are Protective Caps on the End of Chromosomes, Cell, Chromosome and DNA Vector Illustration.* Image. https://www.shutterstock.com/image-vector/telomeres-protective-caps-on-end-chromosomes-710795275 .

- *West, Michael D.* "Dr. Alexey Olovnikov Explains His Conception of the Telomere Hypothesis of Cell Aging." 2017. Video. https://www.youtube.com/watch?v=w_uS-kmHvwo.

- West, Michael. *The Immortal Cell.* New York: Doubleday, 2003.

CHAPTER 6: SENESCENT CELLS

- "Great Results." *Oisín Biotechnologies*, June 3, 2020. https://www.oisinbio.com/#great-results.

- Herper, Matthew. "A Biotech Entrepreneur Aims to Help Us Stay Young While Growing Old." *Forbes*, 2018. https://www.forbes.com/sites/matthewherper/2018/06/05/how-a-biotech-entrepreneur-aims-to-make-aging-less-awful/#4c51820e2c20.

- Hayflick, Leonard, and Paul S. Moorhead. "The Serial Cultivation of Human Diploid Cell Strains." *Experimental Cell Research* 25, no. 3 (1961): 585-621. https://pubmed.ncbi.nlm.nih.gov/13905658/

- "How Age-Damaged Mitochondria Cause Your Cells to Age-Damage You." *Fighting Aging* (blog). 2006. https://

www.fightaging.org/archives/2006/10/how-age-damaged-mitochondria-cause-your-cells-to-damage-you/.

- Sinclair, David. *Lifespan: Why We Age—and Why We Don't Have To.* New York: Atria Publishing Group, 2019.

- "Unity Biotechnology, Inc. Announces First Patient Dosed in Phase 2 Study of ubx0101 in Osteoarthritis of the Knee." *Unity Biotechnology,* 2019. http://ir.unitybiotechnology.com/news-releases/news-release-details/unity-biotechnology-inc-announces-first-patient-dosed-phase-2.

- "Unity Biotechnology, Inc. Common Stock." Nasdaq. Accessed July 5, 2020. https://www.nasdaq.com/market-activity/stocks/ubx

CHAPTER 7: GENOMIC INSTABILITY

- Brenner, Charles, and Noah T. Fluharty. "Fat Mobilization without Weight Loss Is a Potentially Rapid Response to Nicotinamide Riboside in Obese People: It's Time to Test with Exercise." *The American Journal of Clinical Nutrition* (2020). doi:10.1093/ajcn/nqaa109.

- Cummings, Jeffrey L., Travis Morstorf, and Kate Zhong. "Alzheimer's Disease Drug-Development Pipeline: Few Candidates, Frequent Failures." *Alzheimer's Research & Therapy* 6, no. 4 (2020): 37. doi:10.1186/alzrt269.

- "David Sinclair on NMN and Epigenetics." *Life Extension Advocacy Foundation.* September 10, 2019. https://www.lifespan.io/news/an-interview-with-dr-david-sinclair/.

- DiMasi, Joseph A., Henry G. Grabowski, and Ronald W. Hansen. "Innovation in the Pharmaceutical Industry: New Estimates of R&D Costs." *Journal of Health Economics* 47, 20-33 (2016). doi:10.1016/j.jhealeco.2016.01.012.

- Li, Jun, Michael S. Bonkowski, Sébastien Moniot, Dapeng Zhang, et al. "A Conserved NAD+Binding Pocket That Regulates Protein-Protein Interactions During Aging." *Science* 355, no. 6331 (2017): 1312-1317. doi:10.1126/science.aad8242.

- López-Otín, Carlos, Maria A. Blasco, Linda Partridge, Manuel Serrano, et al. "The Hallmarks of Aging." *Cell* 153, no. 6 (2013): 1194-1217. doi:10.1016/j.cell.2013.05.039.

- Moore, Thomas J., Hanzhe Zhang, Gerard Anderson, and G. Caleb Alexander. "Estimated Costs of Pivotal Trials for Novel Therapeutic Agents Approved by the US Food and Drug Administration, 2015-2016." *JAMA Internal Medicine* 178, no.11 (2016): 1451. doi:10.1001/jamainternmed.2018.3931.

- "Nicotinamide Riboside: From Discovery to Human Translation." *Charles Brenner Laboratory.* June 4, 2020. https://brenner.lab.uiowa.edu/current-projects/nicotinamide-riboside-discovery-human-translation.

- Park, Alice. "Scientists Can Reverse DNA Aging in Mice." *TIME*, March 23, 2017. https://time.com/4711023/how-to-keep-your-dna-from-aging/.

- Schultz, Michael B., and David A. Sinclair. "Why NAD + Declines During Aging: It's Destroyed." *Cell Metabolism* 23, no. 6 (2016): 965-966. doi:10.1016/j.cmet.2016.05.022.

- Sinclair, David. *Lifespan: Why We Age—and Why We Don't Have To.* New York: Atria Publishing Group, 2019.

- "Tru Niagen." *Chromadex.* June 4, 2020. https://www.chromadex.com/tru-niagen/.

CHAPTER 8: MITOCHONDRIAL DYSFUNCTION

- "Alzheimer's Drug Candidates Reverse Broader Aging, Study Shows." *Salk Institute for Biological Studies.* 2019. https://www.salk.edu/news-release/alzheimers-drug-candidates-reverse-broader-aging-study-shows/.

- Goldberg, Joshua, Antonio Currais, Marguerite Prior, Wolfgang Fischer, et al. "The Mitochondrial ATP Synthase Is a Shared Drug Target for Aging and Dementia." *Aging Cell* 17, no. 2 (2018): e12715. doi:10.1111/acel.12715.

- Gray, Michael W., Gertraud Burger, and B. Franz Lang. *Genome Biology* 2, no 6 (2001): 1018.1. doi:10.1186/gb-2001-2-6-reviews1018.

- "Mitochondrial DNA." *National Human Genome Institute.* https://www.genome.gov/genetics-glossary/Mitochondrial-DNA.

- "How Age-Damaged Mitochondria Cause Your Cells to Age-Damage You." *Fighting Aging* (blog). 2006. https://www.fightaging.org/archives/2006/10/how-age-damaged-mitochondria-cause-your-cells-to-damage-you/.

- Lodish, H, A. Berk, and S.L. Zipursky. *Molecular Cell Biology.* 4th ed. New York: W. H. Freeman, 2020.

- López-Otín, Carlos, Maria A. Blasco, Linda Partridge, Manuel Serrano, et al. "The Hallmarks of Aging." *Cell* 153, no. 6 (2013): 1194-1217. doi:10.1016/j.cell.2013.05.039.

- Prior, Marguerite, Richard Dargusch, Jennifer L. Ehren, Chandramouli Chiruta, et al. "The Neurotrophic Compound J147 Reverses Cognitive Impairment in Aged Alzheimer's Disease Mice." *Alzheimer's Research & Therapy* 5, no. 3 (2013): 25. doi:10.1186/alzrt179.

- "Salt Institute—J147." *Rejuvenation Roadmap.* Accessed June 5, 2020. https://www.lifespan.io/road-maps/the-rejuvenation-roadmap/salk-institute-j147.

- "Salk Scientists Develop Drug That Slows Alzheimer's in Mice." *Salk Institute for Biological Studies.* 2013. https://www.salk.edu/news-release/salk-scientists-develop-drug-that-slows-alzheimers-in-mice/.

CHAPTER 9: LOSS OF PROTEOSTASIS

- "An Interview with Doug Ethell of Leucadia Therapeutics." *Fighting Aging* (blog). September 10, 2017. https://www.fightaging.org/archives/2017/12/an-interview-with-doug-ethell-of-leucadia-therapeutics/.

- Chun, Diane. "First Sign Of Parkinson's Hit Fox During Filming." *The Gainesville Sun,* 2009. https://www.gainesville.com/article/LK/20090515/News/604148993/GS/

- Cummings, Jeffrey L., Travis Morstorf, and Kate Zhong. "Alzheimer's Disease Drug-Development Pipeline: Few Candidates, Frequent Failures." *Alzheimer's Research & Therapy* 6, no. 4 (2020): 37. doi:10.1186/alzrt269.

- "Facts and Figures." *Alzheimer's Association.* 2020. https://www.alz.org/alzheimers-dementia/facts-figures.

- Kolata, Gina. "An Alzheimer's Treatment Fails: 'We Don't Have Anything Now.'" *The New York Times*, 2020. https://www.nytimes.com/2020/02/10/health/alzheimers-amyloid-drug.html.

- López-Otín, Carlos, Maria A. Blasco, Linda Partridge, Manuel Serrano, et al. "The Hallmarks of Aging." *Cell* 153, no. 6 (2013): 1194-1217. doi:10.1016/j.cell.2013.05.039.

- "Loss of Proteostasis." *Life Extension Advocacy Foundation.* June 4, 2020. https://www.lifespan.io/aging-loss-of-proteostasis/.

- "Michael J. Fox Testimony before the Senate." TV program. Aired 1999. C-SPAN.

- "Primary Care Physicians on the Front Lines of Diagnosing and Providing Alzheimer's and Dementia Care: Half Say Medical Profession Not Prepared to Meet Expected Increase in Demands." *Alzheimer's Association*, 2020. https://www.alz.org/news/2020/primary-care-physicians-on-the-front-lines-of-diag.

- Rocca, Walter A. "The Burden of Parkinson's Disease: A Worldwide Perspective." *The Lancet Neurology* 17, no. 11 (2018): 928-929. doi:10.1016/s1474-4422(18)30355-7.

- Schneider, Karen S. "After the Tears." *People*, 1998. https://people.com/archive/cover-story-after-the-tears-vol-50-no-21/.

- "The Michael J. Fox Foundation for Parkinson's Research." June 4, 2020. https://www.michaeljfox.org/.

- "Treatment Horizon." *Alzheimer's Association.* June 4, 2020. https://www.alz.org/alzheimers-dementia/research_progress/treatment-horizon.

CHAPTER 10: DEREGULATED NUTRIENT SENSING

- Centers for Disease Control and Prevention. "Chronic Kidney Disease Basics." Accessed June 2, 2020. https://www.cdc.gov/kidneydisease/basics.html.

- Dubal, Dena B., Jennifer S. Yokoyama, Lei Zhu, Lauren Broestl, et al. "Life Extension Factor Klotho Enhances Cognition." *Cell Reports* 7, no. 4 (2014): 1065-1076. doi:10.1016/j.celrep.2014.03.076.

- "Hormone Could Lead to a Fountain of Youth Research." *Los Angeles Time,.* 2005. https://www.latimes.com/archives/la-xpm-2005-aug-27-sci-aging27-story.html.

- Hu, Ming Chang, Mingjun Shi, Nancy Gillings, Brianna Flores, et al. "Recombinant A-Klotho May Be Prophylactic and Therapeutic for Acute to Chronic Kidney Disease Progression and Uremic Cardiomyopathy." *Kidney International* 91, no. 5 (2017): 1104-1114. doi:10.1016/j.kint.2016.10.034.

- López-Otín, Carlos, Maria A. Blasco, Linda Partridge, Manuel Serrano, and Guido Kroemer. "The Hallmarks of Aging." *Cell* 153, no. 6 (2013): 1194-1217. doi:10.1016/j.cell.2013.05.039.

- Morphart Creation. "The three fates of Greek Mythology." Image. Accessed July 5, 2020. https://www.shutterstock.com/image-vector/three-fates-greek-mythology-were-sisters-1400994110.

- "The Fates." *Greekmythology.com.* June 5, 2020 https://www.greekmythology.com/Other_Gods/The_Fates/the_fates.html.

- Zhou, Xiangxiang, Xiaosheng Fang, Yujie Jiang, Lingyun Geng, et al. "Klotho, an Anti-Aging Gene, Acts as a Tumor Suppressor and Inhibitor Of IGF-1R Signaling in Diffuse Large B Cell Lymphoma." *Journal Of Hematology & Oncology,* 10 no. 1 (2017). doi:10.1186/s13045-017-0391-5.

CHAPTER 11: ALTERED INTERCELLULAR COMMUNICATIONS

- "Amy Wagers, PhD" *Harvard Stem Cell Institute.* Accessed March 30, 2020. https://hsci.harvard.edu/people/amy-wagers-phd.

- *Blood Countess: Elizabeth Bathory, Anonymous Portrait, 17th Century.* History Today. Image. https://www.historytoday.com/archive/months-past/death-countess-elizabeth-bathory.

- Brodwin, Erin. "A Controversial Startup That Charges $8,000 to Fill Your Veins with Young Blood Now Claims to Be Up and Running in 5 Cities across the US." *Business Insider*, 2019. https://www.businessinsider.com/young-blood-transfusions-open-accepting-paypal-payments-cities-ambrosia-2019-1.

- Cavendish, Richard. "Death of Countess Elizabeth Bathory." *History Today*, 2014. https://www.historytoday.com/archive/months-past/death-countess-elizabeth-bathory.

- Chen, Angela. "Everything Wrong with the Young Blood Injection Craze." *The Verge*, 2019. https://www.theverge.com/2019/3/26/18280967/young-blood-food-drug-administration-health-aging-longevity-parabiosis-science.

- Gayle, Damien. "North Korean Dictator Kim Il-Sung Thought Transfusions of Blood from Youths Would Help Him Live to 100." *The Daily Mail*, 2014. https://www.dailymail.co.uk/news/article-2800178/from-watching-children-play-blood-transfusions-youths-bizarre-treatments-pursued-north-koreas-founder-kim-il-sung-bid-live-100.html.

- "Irina M. Conboy's Research While Affiliated with University of California, Berkeley and Other Places." *Researchgate*. Accessed June 6, 2020. https://www.researchgate.net/scientific-contributions/38824012_Irina_M_Conboy.

- "Irving L. Weissman." *Researchgate*. Accessed June 6, 2020. https://www.researchgate.net/profile/Irving_Weissman.

- Malathronas, John. "'Blood Countess' in Slovakia: Tourists on the Trail of Elizabeth Bathory." *CNN*, 2014. https://www.cnn.com/travel/article/blood-countess-slovakia/index.html.

- "Michael Conboy." *Researchgate*. Accessed June 6, 2020. https://www.researchgate.net/profile/Michael_Conboy3 .

- Rebo, Justin, Melod Mehdipour, Ranveer Gathwala, Keith Causey, et al. "A Single Heterochronic Blood Exchange Reveals Rapid Inhibition of Multiple Tissues by Old Blood." *Nature Communications* 7, no. 1 (2016). doi:10.1038/ncomms13363.

- "Selected Publications." *Rando Laboratory*. Accessed March 30. 2020 http://randolab.stanford.edu/publication/.

- "The Conboy Laboratory." *Berkeley Engineering*. Accessed April 5. 2020 http://conboylab.berkeley.edu/.

- The Florida Institute for Human & Machine Cognition. "Episode 91: Irina and Michael Conboy Explain Tissue Repair and Stem-Cell Rejuvenation." Accessed June 27, 2020. In *STEM—Talk*. Podcast. https://www.ihmc.us/stemtalk/episode-91/.

- "Tony Wyss-Coray." *Researchgate*. 2020. https://www.researchgate.net/profile/Tony_Wyss-Coray.

CHAPTER 12: STEM CELL EXHAUSTION

- Balza Jr., Robert. "The Holy Grail of Medicine—A Look at Ethical Stem Cell Research." *Christian Life Resources*. Accessed June 4, 2020. https://christianliferesources.com/2018/05/14/the-holy-grail-of-medicine-a-look-at-ethical-stem-cell-research/.

- Cafasso, Jacquelyn. "How Many Cells Are in the Human Body? Fast Facts." *Healthline*. 2018. https://www.healthline.com/health/number-of-cells-in-body#types-of-cells.

- Eveleth, Rose. "There Are 37.2 Trillion Cells in Your Body." *The Smithsonian Magazine*, 2013. https://www.smithsonianmag.com/smart-news/there-are-372-trillion-cells-in-your-body-4941473/.

- "Facts and Myths." *American Transplant Foundation*. Accessed June 4. 2020 https://www.americantransplantfoundation.org/about-transplant/facts-and-myths/.

- Hufford, Michael. "Dean Kamen—Dean of Invention—Lygenesis Overview." 2017. Video. https://www.youtube.com/watch?v=mVEROAZB9gs&t=2s.

- "Introduction: What Are Stem Cells, and Why Are They Important?" *National Institutes of Health*. Accessed June 4, 2020. https://stemcells.nih.gov/info/basics/I.htm.

- López-Otín, Carlos, Maria A. Blasco, Linda Partridge, Manuel Serrano, and Guido Kroemer. "The Hallmarks Of Aging." *Cell* 153, no. 6 (2013): 1194-1217. doi:10.1016/j.cell.2013.05.039.

- Piore, Adam. "Big Idea: Turning Lymph Nodes into Liver-Growing Factories." *Discover*. 2012. https://www.discovermagazine.com/technology/big-idea-turning-lymph-nodes-into-liver-growing-factories.

- "Shinya Yamanaka Biographical." *The Nobel Prize Foundation.* Accessed June 4, 2020 https://www.nobelprize.org/prizes/medicine/2012/yamanaka/biographical/.

- "The Promise of Induced Pluripotent Stem Cells (IPSCs)." *The National Institutes of Health.* Accessed June 4, 2020. https://stemcells.nih.gov/info/Regenerative_Medicine/2006Chapter10.htm .

- Turner, Ben. "Exclusive Profile: Lygenesis and Growing Ectopic Organs." *Longevity Technology.* Accessed June 4, 2020. https://www.discovermagazine.com/technology/big-idea-turning-lymph-nodes-into-liver-growing-factories.

- Yeomans, Mike. "Lygenesis Out to Prove the Age of Organ Regeneration Has Arrived." *University of Pittsburgh Innovation Institute.* Accessed June 4, 2020 https://www.innovation.pitt.edu/record-breaking-pitt-startup-flipping-the-script-on-organ-transplantation/.

CHAPTER 13: EPIGENETIC ALTERATIONS

- Bell, Jordana T., and Tim D. Spector. "A Twin Approach to Unraveling Epigenetics." *Trends in Genetics* 27, no. 3: (2011): 116-125. https://doi.org/10.1016/j.tig.2010.12.005

- Burbridge, David. "Francis Galton on Twins, Heredity and Social Class." *The British Journal For the History of Science* 34, no. 3 (2001): 323-340. https://www.jstor.org/stable/4028101.

- Chen, Edwin. "Twins Reared Apart: A Living Lab." *The New York Times*, December 9, 1979. https://www.nytimes.com/1979/12/09/archives/twins-reared-apart-a-living-lab.html.

- Cowell, Ian. "Epigenetics–It's Not Just Genes That Make Us." *British Society for Cell Biology*. Accessed June 5, 2020. https://bscb.org/learning-resources/softcell-e-learning/epigenetics-its-not-just-genes-that-make-us/#:~:text=Quick%20look%3A%20In%20its%20modern,traits%20of%20a%20whole%20organism.

- Hill, Steve. "An Interview with Prof. Vittorio Sebastiano of Turn.Bio." *Life Extension Advocacy Foundation*. April 4, 2020. https://www.lifespan.io/news/an-interview-with-prof-vittorio-sebastiano-of-turn-bio/#:~:text=Vittorio%20Sebastiano%20of,Bio&text=Bio%2C%20a%20company%20developing%20partial,a%20primary%20reason%20we%20age.

- Moore, Thomas J., Hanzhe Zhang, Gerard Anderson, and G. Caleb Alexander. "Estimated Costs of Pivotal Trials for Novel Therapeutic Agents Approved by the US Food and Drug Administration, 2015-2016." *JAMA Internal Medicine* 178, no.11 (2016): 1451. doi:10.1001/jamainternmed.2018.3931.

- "Nature vs. Nurture Theory (Genes vs. Environment) Center." *MedicineNet*. Last modified July 25, 2017. https://www.medicinenet.com/nature_vs_nurture_theory_genes_or_environment/index.htm.

- Ocampo, Alejandro, Pradeep Reddy, Paloma Martinez-Redondo, Aida Platero-Luengo, et al. "In Vivo Amelioration of

Age-Associated Hallmarks by Partial Reprogramming." *Cell* 167, issue 7 (2016). https://doi.org/10.1016/j.cell.2016.11.052.

- Ocampo, Alejandro, Pradeep Reddy, Paloma Martinez-Redondo, Aida Platero-Luengo, et al. "Turning Back Time: Salk Scientists Reverse Signs of Aging." *Salk Institute for Biological Studies*. December 15, 2016. https://www.salk.edu/news-release/turning-back-time-salk-scientists-reverse-signs-aging/.

- Sarkar, Tapash Jay, Marco Quarta, Shravani Mukherjee, Alex Colville, Patrick Paine, Linda Doan, Christopher M. Tran et al. "Transient Non-Integrative Expression of Nuclear Eeprogramming Factors Promotes Multifaceted Amelioration of Aging in Human Cells." *Nature Communications* 11, no. 1 (2020): 1-12.

- Sinclair, David. *Lifespan: Why We Age—and Why We Don't Have To*. New York: Atria Publishing Group, 2019.

PART 3: FINDING THE FOUNTAIN

CHAPTER 14: THE CONSEQUENCES OF LIVING LONGER

- Aging Analytics Agency, "National Longevity Development Plans: Global Overview 2019". http://analytics.dkv.global/data/pdf/National-Longevity-Development-Plans-First-Edition/Report.pdf.

- Centers for Disease Control and Prevention. "Obesity and Overweight." Updated June 13, 2006. https://www.cdc.gov/nchs/fastats/obesity-overweight.htm.

- Conrad, Zach, Meredith T. Niles, Deborah A. Neher, Eric D. Roy, Nicole E. Tichenor, and Lisa Jahns. "Relationship Between Food Waste, Diet Quality, and Environmental Sustainability." *PLOS One*. April 18, 2018. https://doi.org/10.1371/journal.pone.0195405.

- "Food Waste FAQs." US Department of Agriculture. Accessed June 8, 2020. https://www.usda.gov/foodwaste/faqs#:~:text=In%20the%20United%20States%2C%20food,worth%20of%20food%20in%202010.

- Gates, Bill and Melinda Gates. "10 Tough Questions We Get Asked." *Gates Notes* (blog). February 13, 2018. https://www.gatesnotes.com/2018-Annual-Letter?WT.mc_id=02_13_2018_02_AnnualLetter2018_Explainer_BG-YT_&WT.tsrc=BGYT.

- "Goal 2: Zero Hunger." United Nations. Accessed June 8, 2020. https://www.un.org/sustainabledevelopment/hunger/.

- Gray, Richard. "How Can We Manage Earth's Land?" *BBC*. June 29, 2017. https://www.bbc.com/future/article/20170628-how-to-best-manage-earths-land.

- "Livestock and Landscapes." The Food and Agriculture Organization of the United Nations. Accessed June 8, 2020. http://www.fao.org/3/ar591e/ar591e.pdf.

- "Meat and Animal Feed." Agriculture at a Crossroads. Accessed June 8, 2020. https://www.globalagriculture.org/report-topics/meat-and-animal-feed.html.

- "Obesity Projections Worse Than Terrorism Threat for Future—And We Can Do Something about It." *Women's Health Research Institute* (blog). Accessed June 27, 2020. http://www.womenshealth.northwestern.edu/blog/obesity-projections-worse-terrorism-threat-future-and-we-can-do-something-about-it.

- Robin-Champigneul, François. "Jeanne Calment's Unique 122-Year Lifespan: Facts and Factors; Longevity History in Her Genealogical Tree." *Rejuvenation Research* 23 No.1 (February 17, 2020): 19-47. http://doi.org/10.1089/rej.2019.2298.

- Roser, Max, Hannah Ritchie, and Esteban Ortiz-Ospina. *World Population by Region Projected to 2100, 1950 to 2100.* Our World Data. Figure. https://ourworldindata.org/grapher/historical-and-projected-population-by-region.

- Shieber, Jonathan. "Lab-Grown Meat Could Be on Store Shelves by 2022, Thanks to Future Meat Technologies." *Tech Crunch* (blog), October 10, 2019. https://techcrunch.com/2019/10/10/lab-grown-meat-could-be-on-store-shelves-by-2022-thanks-to-future-meat-technologies/.

- Social Security, Status of the Social Security and Medicare Programs. "A Summary of the 2019 Annual Reports." 2019. https://www.ssa.gov/oact/TRSUM/2019/index.html.

- "United Nations, Department of Economic and Social Affairs, Population Division." *World Population Prospects: The 2015 Revision, Volume II: Demographic Profiles.* Accessed June 27, 2020. https://population.un.org/wpp/Publications/Files/WPP2015_Volume-II-Demographic-Profiles.pdf.

- United States Census Bureau. "Older People Projected to Outnumber Children for First Time in US History." March 13, 2018. https://www.census.gov/newsroom/press-releases/2018/cb18-41-population-projections.html.

- United States Department of Agriculture (USDA), National Agricultural Statistics Service (NASS), Agricultural Statistics Board. *Cattle.* January 31, 2020. https://downloads.usda.library.cornell.edu/usda-esmis/files/h702q636h/rb68xv24k/76537h73d/catl0120.pdf

CHAPTER 15: UNLOCKING BIOTECH'S POTENTIAL

- "Alzheimer's Research Funding at the NIH." Alzheimer's Impact Movement. 2019. https://alzimpact.org/issues/research.

- Centers for Disease Control and Prevention. "2017-2018 Estimated Influenza Illnesses, Medical Visits, Hospitalizations, and Deaths and Estimated Influenza Illnesses, Medical Visits, Hospitalizations, and Deaths Averted by Vaccination in the United States." Last modified November 22, 2019. https://www.cdc.gov/flu/about/burden-averted/2017-2018.htm#:~:text=CDC%20estimates%20that%20the%20burden,from%20influenza%20(Table%201).

- Centers for Disease Control and Prevention. "Interim Clinical Guidance for Management of Patients with Confirmed Coronavirus Disease (COVID-19)." Updated June 2, 2020. https://www.cdc.gov/coronavirus/2019-ncov/hcp/clinical-guidance-management-patients.html.

- Centers for Disease Control and Prevention. "Leading Causes of Death." Last modified March 17, 2017. https://www.cdc.gov/nchs/fastats/leading-causes-of-death.htm.

- Comito, Kieth, and Arkadi Mazin. "Aging Is the Foremost Risk Factor for COVID-19. Let's Fight It." *Life Extension Advocacy Foundation*, April 13, 2020. https://www.lifespan.io/news/aging-is-the-foremost-risk-factor-for-covid-19-lets-fight-it/.

- Demetri, George D. "Public Funding Is the Lifeblood of Cancer Research." *Cancer Today*, December 21, 2018. https://www.cancertodaymag.org/Pages/Winter2018-2019/Public-Funding-is-the-Lifeblood-of-Cancer-Research.aspx#:~:text=In%20September%202018%2C%20Congress%20passed,cancer%20patients%20and%20all%20Americans.

- HHS Press Office. "Trump Administration Announces Framework and Leadership for 'Operation Warp Speed,'" *HHS.gov, US Department of Health and Human Services,* May 15, 2020. https://www.hhs.gov/about/news/2020/05/15/trump-administration-announces-framework-and-leadership-for-operation-warp-speed.html.

- Lichfield, Gideon. "Editor's Letter: Old Age Is Over—If You Want It." *MIT Technology Review*, August 21, 2019. https://www.technologyreview.com/2019/08/21/133329/editors-letter-old-age-is-overif-you-want-it.

- Nuland, Sherwin. "Do You Want to Live Forever?" *MIT Technology Review*, February 1, 2005. https://www.technologyreview.com/2005/02/01/231686/do-you-want-to-live-forever/.

- Pontin, Jason. "Is Defeating Aging Only a Dream?" *MIT Technology Review*, July 11, 2006. https://www2. technologyreview.com/sens/#:~:text=Last%20year%2C%20 Technology%20Review%20announced,unworthy%20of%20 learned%20debate.%22%20The.

- Pontin, Jason. "The SENS Challenge." *MIT Technology Review*, July 28, 2005. https://www.technologyreview. com/2005/07/28/230587/the-sens-challenge.

- Schwartz, Steven, Hanyu Ni, Robert N. Anderson, Elizabeth Arias, and Arialdi Miniño. "Deaths: Final Data For 2017." *National Vital Statistics Reports, Centers for Disease Control and Prevention, National Center for Health Statistic.* Accessed June 27, 2020. https://www.cdc.gov/nchs/data/nvsr/nvsr68/ nvsr68_09-508.pdf.

- Shepardson, David. "GM, Philips to Supply 73,000 US Ventilators in $1.1 Billion Effort." *Reuters*, April 8, 2020. https://www.reuters.com/article/us-health-coronavirus-gm/ gm-philips-to-supply-73000-us-ventilators-in-11-billion-effort- idUSKBN21Q1YA.

- Taylor, Derrick Bryson. "How the Coronavirus Pandemic Unfolded: A Timeline." *The New York Times*, June 9, 2020. https://www.nytimes.com/article/coronavirus-timeline.html.

- "US Federal Funding for HIV/AIDS: Trends over Time." *Kaiser Family Foundation*, March 05, 2019. https://www.kff.org/ hivaids/fact-sheet/u-s-federal-funding-for-hivaids-trends- over-time.

- Van Dam, Andrew. "The US Has Thrown More Than $6 Trillion at the Coronavirus Crisis. That Number Could Grow." *Washington Post*, April 15, 2020. https://www.washingtonpost.com/business/2020/04/15/coronavirus-economy-6-trillion.

Made in the USA
Coppell, TX
23 January 2021

48676933R00134